BY CURTIS BOK

STAR WORMWOOD (1959)

I TOO, NICODEMUS (1946)

BACKBONE OF THE HERRING (1941)

These are BORZOI BOOKS
published in New York by ALFRED A. KNOPF

Star Wormwood

"So

Did the Star Wormwood in a blazing fall

Frighten awhile the waters and lie lost.

So did this old woe fade from memory:

Till after, in the fulness of the days,

I needs must find an ember yet unquenched,

And, breathing, blow the spark to flame. It lives,

If precious be the soul of man to man."

◇◇

BROWNING: *The Ring and the Book*

Star Wormwood

BY

CURTIS BOK

1959   *Alfred A. Knopf*   NEW YORK

L. C. Catalog card number: 59–5427
© Curtis Bok, 1959

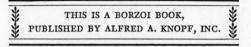

THIS IS A BORZOI BOOK,
PUBLISHED BY ALFRED A. KNOPF, INC.

FIRST EDITION

TO

MARY CURTIS ZIMBALIST

CONTENTS

The commentary following each of the sections is based on three WILLIAM H. WHITE *lectures delivered by the author at the University of Virginia Law School, April 1957.*

Star Wormwood

I

The Crime

IT MAY ALL have begun when Roger was a little boy, playing with his father. To the end of his short life his father remained a dim but pleasant memory, and their game was clear, down the years. His father would nuzzle his neck and say that he would eat him. Roger would cry delightedly that he couldn't. Father replied that he could but he wouldn't, and when this had gone on a satisfying length of time, Roger would clinch the argument: "You couldn't. I'm too big. Part of me would stick out."

If the senior Roger could have been blamed for calling forth such an odd response, he avoided the issue by dying while the boy was still small and without leaving him any brother or sister. Neither, as a lawyer of average ability, did he leave his wife and son an adequate inheritance. It never occurred to Roger to blame his father, even when Dr. Danby dug deeply enough into him to come upon the little game. Roger had a clean feeling that the notion of being left partly sticking out had come from him alone, his unique fate to starve or be eaten.

The times were thin. Born just before the First World War, Roger was on scant rations from the time of American entrance until well after the depression that followed the war. His mother had been badly handled at his birth and was barren thereafter. This exactly suited a businessman who met her while in town attending a convention and who was eager for his pleasure without the ensuing responsibility. She married him when Roger was about ten and followed him to his distant home, leaving Roger with her older sister, Lillie. A few sporadic payments arrived for the boy's support and then ceased, and the sister's requests for help went unanswered.

The fantastic prosperity of the late years of the decade after the war did not filter down to salesgirls generally or to Lillie Dobson in particular, and when the great depression began and settled down upon the nation, it became a matter almost of life or death to hold a job of any kind, even at reduced wages. Roger's aunt soon became expendable both to industry and to life. Late in 1930, at age seventeen, Roger found himself alone, without assets, and without a job. Letters to his mother at the last address he knew were returned unclaimed.

Fortunately for him, he was not too demanding. He had no ambition and not much personality, except a certain wistfulness, which made him look thin, and an aptitude for loneliness, which made him seem morose. Both traits were undeveloped and were like two cups, one empty and the other more than full. Had he been exposed to great art or other high human effort, he might have recognized it as territory designed for the lives of separate and lonely human beings. But he did not live in the way of such things and had not otherwise achieved an equivalent balance in seventeen years. If he had any quality showing the grain of maturity, it was a preference for quiet things that was rarely satisfied. The town in which he lived was on the seacoast, and in times of storm he hated the whole noisy process—the rut of the sea, the shattering roar of the waves, the chant and howl of the wind. It was as if all of nature were in turmoil and bent upon his destruction. The pattern of islands offshore made a tidal funnel which created an almost continual roost, a soft cat-footed lapping on calm days but a great noise like the crushing of stones when

there was wind and scend. Only at slack tide and for fifteen minutes on either side, perhaps an hour in all, was
there peace on fair days. At such times he would wander
about on the beach and lie at length upon a ledge, gazing down into craggy tide pools and imagining tall and
lovely ships upon them.

All of Roger that mattered poured into these times of
quiet, as if the major current of his nature were being
set. It was a kind of tidal flow, at flood when silence was
deep but balked and at neap when the universe was
noisy.

Had Roger lived to maturity, he might have seen that
his fumbling between noise and quiet was the ancient
battleground of man. Noise without and peace within, if
it be God's peace, is the fallow of great souls and even
of a Savior. He was too young and frustrated to see this,
hiding his head beneath the covers of his bed when the
rage of noise was on the world, but feeling his spirit
sleep when the air and water were still. Then he could
see to the bottom of his tide pools, and there was no
quiver down to the starfish and periwinkles, and his gal-
leons could float across the tiny deeps and shallows to
his harbors. There, gently, they delivered to him balm
and frankincense and myrrh, and there was only memory of the deeps which they had crossed in silence. But
in real depth there was mystery, and there was fear.

The Crime

Bending above a tide pool, Roger could contemplate the bottom calmly, even when in his imagination it was miles deep, for he could see it clearly and in relation to the shallows and the shore. But when he swam he was terrified to look down through the green water: the glint of bottom far below or the shadowy mass of a rock spelled horror to him. He saw them as unsounded deep that drew him and evil upthrusting stone that reached for him.

His other conflict was the normal one of being the diptych man and woman. Since he died before he was more than half formed, it is difficult to report him very distinctly. He was a very male boy, despite his being small and slight, which was mostly due to hunger, and being quiet, which was not quite normal, due to lack of early male companionship. Even that much is uncertain. All that could be said with clarity is that to a perceptive eye the boy showed signs of having a man's creative imagination based on loneliness, and a woman's reticence, but the only perceptive eye was that of Dr. Danby, the psychiatrist, and then it was too late. Education had done little good, as the public school in the area where Roger and his aunt lived had no perceptive eyes to look as deeply into the boy as discovery of his main stream required. In no other field is there such risk of failure of communication. It was as if the teacher wrote on the blackboard with invisible ink or sifted stones of different sizes through a sieve the size of whose mesh he did not know. Roger was graduated not so much because he passed as because his desk was needed for the next class.

Hunger was the most thorough and persistent of Roger's teachers. Meals with his aunt were slender and indifferently cooked, and it was only when he found infrequent work for an hour or two after school that he could buy a bit of fresh meat or a sweet on which to feast himself.

He had few acquaintances and no friends, for friendship is a profession to be learned and practiced, and Roger had neither time nor inclination and no knowledge of the art of living. Companionship among the group he saw at school and in the streets meant little more than occupying, usually combatively, the same ten square feet of space.

The only friend he cultivated was a boy whom he had come upon one day in the woods after he had finished school. This boy was a stranger, a recent arrival from a farm in the interior of the State, and if it was the solitude of the woods that brought them together, it was the similarity of their last names that held their interest until they found a better reason. Roger's name was Haike and Joe's was Hake. "That's a fish," Roger said, after they had got the matter of spelling straightened out. Joe bridled, thinking it a reflection on him, but Roger explained that it was a good thing to have a food for a name, and he offered to show Joe how to fish. In turn Joe offered to show Roger how to snare rabbits.

They had ample competition. What was usually a sport became a necessity for many people in the depression years. Fishing from the piers and wharves in the town's inadequate harbor was not satisfactory because of the sewage and refuse allowed to flow into it, and at best there was only a small run of fish. Beyond the harbor were miles of straight sandy beach whose gentle slope made for towering waves but little fishing. Near the mouth of the harbor there were a few outcroppings of rock which walled the channel, and a stone pier or two which had fallen into disrepair. If the tide was flooding clean water into the harbor, a few fish might be taken from around the larger rocks and stones. On good days these were crowded with men fishing, and Roger learned to go there in bad weather when there were fewer men, and perhaps fewer fish. It was here, in better times, that he had gone swimming. He had to steel himself against the noise and wash, but he also had to eat. Joe, more aggressive but afraid of falling in because he had never learned to swim, usually competed with the men and rarely joined Roger, but they went together to the woods and fields for rabbit. They kept little for themselves because Joe had a large family and was beaten by his father if he failed to bring in a rabbit with fair regularity. What they kept for themselves they shared, although this right had to be won by battle. Joe thought that he should keep his own rabbits and share Roger's in return for having taught him how to capture them. Like most quiet people, Roger had a rare but savage temper, and the joint pressures of hunger, injustice, and the mastery of a new skill roused him one day to a murderous rage against Joe, who was methodically dividing in half Roger's first rabbit. Joe remembered well that he had suddenly been set upon by a maniac.

Once a workable share of the bag had been settled, the boys got along well enough together. Roger, naturally quiet, and Joe, bred to farm work, were both taciturn, and what verbal expression they did give to their thought was significant. There was no small talk and whatever was said was designed to advance the situation.

They borrowed each other's mood, as quiet people do. As an introvert, Roger knew that in the presence of his neighbor and of himself as well man leads a double life and must stand strongly up to both if he can. It was not necessary to his continual state of physical famine to remind himself that part of him or of a monstrous meal might stick out. He was as afraid of any part of thought whose end he could not see as he was of the bottom of the harbor entrance that he could see when swimming. It obsessed him, the fear of distance and noise within or without him, and absorbed much of his normal energy.

Joe, despite the extrovert's uneasy feeling that there might be something more than met the eye, had no such inhibitions. His parents, in begetting and conceiving him, may as well have been a tree and a fallow field. His reactions to life were direct and earthy. To snare nature or be snared by it were the same process, and he had no moral judgment for what to him was one thing. He was of Roger's age, large and strong in physique and as yet an underling in will. He had been unable to withstand the terrible thrust of Roger's anger at sharing rabbits, and, despite his greater size and strength, could do no more than beat off the rush of his furious little adversary. He was frightened by naked emotion. Hence he was frightened by the passion of his younger sister when she stripped herself before him one evening and dared him to lie with her. Joe's feelings at that moment were in a state of panic. He was large, innocent, and sixteen. His sister was well formed, evil, and thirteen.

She had the incongruous name of Angela and had learned the lexicon of sex at school and in the streets. The passionately precocious attract it like a magnet. And her home, with its creaking bedsprings and the su-

perimposed bodes of her parents, completed the picture.
She had only to choose a Saturday night after the aphro-
disiac bath. Joe was emerging from the tub when the
bathroom door, which Angela had learned to pick with
a hairpin, opened and disclosed her, black eyes flashing
and worn bathrobe half open. Never dropping her eyes
from his, she discarded this single garment and advanced upon him.

The struggle was short. Joe's mixture of shame, horror, and confusion was soon leveled by a pair of warm
and searching lips.

He found himself standing there, facing a naked girl.
That she was his young sister seemed not to matter.

From then on they developed in opposite directions.
She had won her battle with him and after a month or
two of wild and frequent intercourse she began to lose
interest, not so much in the sexual act as in him. He, on
the other hand, grew in the desire to have her and none
other. Not that he had ever had another, and hence Angela found herself in the position of having won the battle and lost the war. When cold and prepossessed, she
threatened not to let him near her again. He threatened
to tell their parents. Frightened and still half drawn to
him, she gave herself, but no longer wholly. Feeling her
passion for him cooling, he became more savage and insistent.

Their relationship as brother and sister at first made impossible any mutual feeling but passion, which is essentially impersonal. Only rare people can carry their love undiminished through the act of love. In the following period of slack tide woman creeps closer for security, but man resumes the warrior's wariness or he sleeps. The only mutuality of feeling between Joe and Angela was that of conspirators, and because their passion imprisoned them it soon became hatred.

In such primitive areas animals achieve a cunning knowledge of each other's moods. Angela knew that she had to break away from Joe. Passionate as she was, she had grown frightened of the dreadful power of the frantic male above her. She had not counted on unleashing such focused strength as this. She began to feel bruised and to fear that in his frenzy he would fail to protect her. She had a young girl's fear of pain and of the greater, unknown torture of childbirth. Joe knew that she must not become pregnant, but she saw him no longer as her brother but as a monstrous and dangerous stranger. They had no money for preventatives.

While he was with her one evening she knew that she must make the final break. She had no plan beyond running away, and in her frightened state she decided then and there to do so. As if the decision changed her whole responsive mechanism, Joe felt it. He wanted to keep her as a source of pleasure, and battling her was giving him sadistic satisfaction in the whole campaign, but if she meant to stop the fun he would get even with her. She was thrusting at him to get him off her, but he brushed her aside with an ugly laugh and redoubled his efforts. Then she guessed what he was up to and began desperately biting and scratching him. He knew the time had come to play his last card, if he was to beat her.

"There, damn you!" he muttered, rolling away from her. She slobbered curses at him and kicked him, arranging her clothes, and burst out of the house.

Angela ran aimlessly through the streets for some time, but slowed down as a host of thoughts swarmed into her mind. Soon it would be visible and her parents would have to know. She would tell them it was Joe, and the sweet thought of revenge warmed her a little. Then it occurred to her that one emission might not take. But this passed in the fright of what the nine months and the birth would be like. She thought of abortions, of being sent away, but mostly she thought of the lack of money at home, and of death. She was only thirteen, and she would surely die: you had to be a woman to give birth and live. There was no money for an operation, and she had heard stories of homemade abortions which invariably brought poisoning and death. Death seemed to close every door she turned to, and she began running again, her face so white and agonized that the few people she passed looked at her curiously. She must seek death herself, quickly. She did not know how, but it must be quick and not the long and tortuous death suggested by every other choice of action.

It was too much for her young mind to take in at once. She saw no clear path, even to death by her own hand. Her mind sheered off to an easier emotion, hatred of Joe and soon of all mankind for its cruelty and its traps. She could remember no responsibility of her own or any part of the process with her brother save his final act of betrayal and the mounting strength of will that led him to it. He had beaten her at the one point where she had had to trust him. Hatred of Joe spread to hatred of all men: she could not die without devising a fitting act of revenge upon some one of them.

It was a Sunday evening in late winter, the weather warming but still raw. Angela was trembling and in need of shelter, but greater than the need of warmth was the need of revenge. But on whom? Joe was already fused with her parents in her mind, and together they were too many for her. Beyond that, victims ready-made for a thirteen-year-old girl's revenge seemed not to exist in great numbers or in convenient places. By instinct she turned her steps toward her school. It might be open and at least she could be warm and find a place to think. As she visualized the interior of the building, she remembered that the friend of Joe's with the same name had recently got a job there as a substitute janitor and watchman. If she could find him, something would occur to her.

Reaching the school, she went to the janitor's door and tried it. It was open, and she entered. She stood for a moment, letting her eyes become accustomed to the darkness, although she knew the basement well, from having used it for sexual experiments with various fellow pupils, both girls and boys. Then she saw a glow from the furnace room and went softly toward it. When she reached the door she had a full view of Roger balancing on a furnace rake the dead body of a small animal and pushing it carefully forward over the glowing coals.

Her eyes narrowed with sudden decision and she stepped inside.

The best part of Roger's life was the period from his graduation from high school to the night when Angela appeared in the basement. The best part of Lillie's was after Roger came to live with her.

She had never married. Work had been an early and continuous obsession, and she was so reserved that any expression of emotion in her presence made her ill. She held such a tight rein on her own that she gave no rewards whatsoever to men and had been unable to do more than look levelly at the few who had looked at her. It was not that she could not feel but that she could not give, and the one man who had seemed to see farther into her than the others and to want the fine fidelity that was there was at length unable to stand being stared at, not spoken to, and held off. Lillie did not repulse him and she could not welcome him: she simply created a wasteland between them and maintained it, she on one side and he on the other. If he pushed toward her, she withdrew as instinctively as a tooth nerve retreats before an advancing cavity. It may have been that she did not know how to offer her fidelity or, which is harder, to accept another's, and instinct was too weak in her to arc across the gap.

Lillie's fires were banked low. She was ten years older than Roger's mother and had gone gray early. She had a slight and perpetual cough and an unfocused stare, as if she had built an opaque defense against the world's show of emotion, which she had learned to look at without seeing.

She could never have borne her nephew's presence if he had been a roaring, noisy boy or if he had been an infant, however quiet. Her insight into herself may have been the sharper for being constantly turned inward and never shared, and often she had given thanks that she had not had a helpless male body to do for. She would not have known how, and sometimes in the evening when there was a scrap of warm ember left in the stove she would sit before it, her back to the room, and blush at her thoughts before she was able to control them and go to bed. She would look at Roger on the way, as if challenging herself with the sight of the well-grown boy who could tend to his own physical needs. It was as near to sex as Lillie ever got. The man who had once looked intently at her had been an advancing problem, blank from the neck down, as Roger now was. Lillie's whole sexual life consisted of her mental image of her nephew's infant body, rendered the more luminous by her imagined inability to cope with it.

When Lillie first got straight in her mind what her feeling for Roger was, she found a perverse hostility to him for no longer being what attracted her most darkly. But, as happens in people of low intensity, shadows are more substantial than substance, and Lillie was soon put right by another shadow which opposed and eclipsed the sexual one: Roger would take the place of the child she could never have brought herself to have, and hence, in her shadow world, she would be fulfilled.

The Crime

Lillie began to live at the top of her low pressure. She no longer tried to discover her sister's whereabouts. This was her life and her sister's forfeit. It was not easy, but she had always had to struggle economically and the added burden of Roger on her thin budget acted as cement to her resolution. Lillie went with relief to the world when her problem was unemotional.

So long as she did not have to express it, she was able to surrender to the idea that Roger meant everything to her.

Roger, in turn, could not have borne his aunt if she had been a roaring, noisy woman intent on shattering him with her glowing affection. Most boys are shamed, bored, and sustained by violent maternal emotion, so that to the end of their lives they utter the sound Mother in a tremulous voice as if it were a holy and self-executing word. The truth, more likely, is that love, even if gross and ordinary, remains the best though still imperfect cure for the world's ills, including its crime.

Roger hardly felt his aunt's affection, that being the price low pressure pays. It expressed itself in ways no ordinary boy would recognize: his thin but well-made cot, the better bit of meat when there was meat, and her gaze, no longer misty and entrenched when she looked at him, but clear and kind. She had no words to go with these things, and his young mind had no feelers with which to capture and savor them.

Yet he felt sustained, since love can do that, but in the conscious reaches of his mind it meant only a safe place to go, and food. He spent his aunt's suppressed love, barely knowing that he had it. All that he felt was gratitude for silence and for an absence of the world's kicks and buffets. They were of the same family and could get along with few words.

His graduation was a high point in their lives. Roger took no prizes, but he was smaller and younger than the average and this gave him a private distinction which they could both enjoy. He had passed his courses tidily if not brilliantly and took his place in the line of students with satisfaction. Lillie, looking at him, felt her achievement at its peak, and there were smaller things to give her an even livelier pride: his boots were well blacked, his hair well cut, his linen clean, and the patch on the trousers of his one dark suit was on his right side and mercifully hidden when the line of students presented only their left. Her Roger looked as well as any of them, and it was plain for all to see.

Afterwards they waited a little while among the students and their families, but no one paid them much attention. They were standing on a path to one side and were in the way of the principal when he came out to mingle with the crowd. Finding himself almost in collision with one of his pupils, he paused and spoke a few words. Lillie was able to acknowledge them only with a bob of her head. Roger produced a grin.

They stood about a bit uncertainly and then went home. Lillie had prepared the best dinner she could, in honor of the occasion, and they sat longer than usual over it, each thinking his own thoughts. Communication seemed complete after each had summed up the morning in a sentence.

"You looked fine," Lillie said. "Imagine Dr. Beechum himself speaking to us."

"Yeah," Roger said. "It all went off fine."

At bedtime she did probably the one impulsive thing of her life. She bent over his chair and kissed him on the forehead. He was so startled that he could only gape and hang his head. Lillie, in a tumult of surprise at herself, went to her room and was ill. When he awoke late in the morning, with no school to go to, his breakfast was standing ready for him. As he ate it he knew that he must find work or do something to help his aunt, although she had not mentioned it.

Lillie lived only a year longer. It was a year of illness

and deterioration, of which healthy boys have a natural horror. The tiny apartment, geared to all of the uses of living except leisure, had little to hold Roger and it felt like a vise upon him. He was tempted to run away, and later, while awaiting death in his turn, he wondered why he had not. Something held him and he knew what it was: his aunt had taken care of him and had asked for no return. He realized that he felt an obligation to share with her what he could find, and in his freedom from school and from any future schedule he found that his obligation gave to his freedom a new and pleasant quality. It was part of the excitement of becoming a man and of doing, for a purpose, whatever pleased him.

He had no reason to disturb the state of reverie in which his aunt seemed increasingly to live. She continued doing for him the basic things that he needed, and if they were shoddy, other people were in no better case. He gave up seeking advice from her or even a point of view, about girls or the authority of the law or how to behave in certain social situations. When he asked her about these things she merely looked startled, and when he pressed his questions she moved wearily away, telling him that she had had no time to learn about things like that and that she was tired. He felt rebuffed but not driven off, for if he failed to understand the reasons for another person's silence, he at least appreciated that there was silence. She neither answered his questions nor lectured him, and he could see that she was ill.

He spent as little time as possible in the apartment. He was on the town most of the time, although the beach was counterfoil to the deadly monotony of the street corners. He did what he could to find work after leaving school, but there were ten trained men for every job that became available, and all that he could get was the kind of momentary task that employers could hire boys to do without having to employ them at steady wages. He and Lillie were pinched but not in want. He came to see the hypocrisy in published statements that prosperity was just around the corner, that men could rise above their condition, and that anyone could find work if he was determined enough. The grim truth became apparent that, no matter how determined a man was, it was possible that no work existed for him. The pious slogans slackened and disappeared as the depression deepened and bit into the country.

The prevailing mood suited Roger and aroused no conflict in him. He was poor and he flowed with the stagnating times, thinking that it was the way things normally were. He heard the black talk of men with wife and children to support, but it meant little to him, since he had none. Feeling no special pressure was a factor in his not turning to theft, the preponderant crime in times of depression. There was no moral issue involved and no victory over temptation: there had been no ground for temptation.

Lillie lost her job through no fault of her own, except that she had been absent a good deal on account of illness. She was laid off because the store in which she was employed lost custom. Someone had to go, and obviously it was the Lillies that went. The survival of the fittest was in evidence, a fine law when applied to the process that keeps insects and animals from overrunning the world, but at cross-purposes with the life of man. Human beings well fitted for some purposes fell because they were unfitted for the bare struggle to survive. Something was very wrong with man's world.

After Lillie lost her job, she and Roger lived for six months from the bread line and the soup kitchen. It was thin fare but sufficient, but as these organizations were privately supported they operated unevenly and had the sticky air of charity about them. Now and then Roger supplied a few fish or a rabbit, for it was during this time that he met Joe. Aside from having somewhat less to eat, life was little different from before.

Then Lillie inconspicuously got pneumonia and died. She vanished like a scarf of ground fog in the early sun. She stayed in bed for several days, but did not know what to ask Roger to do for her. He brought her water to drink and what little food there was left in the cupboard, and since it was all that he could think to do, he left and went to ask help of Mrs. Mason, who lived near by and was as much a friend as Lillie had in town. Mrs. Mason had eight children and no time for nursing Lillie, but she gave him what advice and food she could and he went to the beach to sleep so as not to disturb his aunt. When he came back in the morning he found her delirious and unable to ask for anything. There was no money for a doctor and Roger had no idea what to do for her except to put cold compresses on her forehead as Mrs. Mason had told him. He did this so long that he got tired and then went out to the beach again. He wished his aunt would hurry up and get well: all sick people that he knew got well after a while. He found some wildflowers and took them to the apartment, where he put them beside Lillie's bed, but she only muttered in her fever and when she did open her eyes there was no recognition in them.

She was so sick that Roger was alarmed and decided to stay with her in case she should awake and tell him what to do for her. She would of course be able to do that if she was in any danger. She seemed to get worse, and Roger spent a night and two days watching over her without sleep. She roused a little for necessities of nature

and he supported her frail and barely conscious form to
the bathroom door, where she dismissed him. Once,
when she was getting slowly into bed again, she saw the
flowers and thanked him in a low voice.

At last she was too sick to rise, and once she seemed
to be in distress and to be signaling to him, but before
he could think of how to cope with the situation he became aware that it was too late. He could not bring
himself to remove the bedclothes and look at his aunt's
body and clean her. He could not think how to manage
a dry mattress and sheets and a blanket. His aunt
seemed quieter. Desperately tired, his mind closed
against her troubles. He flung himself on his cot and
was asleep in an instant.

When he awoke the next day there was a difference.
The apartment had a singular stillness and seemed to
have grown a new dimension. He felt the third presence
of death in the room even before he reached his aunt's
bed. Lillie lay in her aromatic wet, her eyes staring a
bit more than in life and her gray hair threaded on the
pillow. Roger's flowers lay on her breast with one of her
hands resting on them.

Death had not come so close to him before and he revolted from it. He ran into the street and told the first
policeman he met.

Lillie was found to have a small insurance policy, and

it ensured her burial. When that was done there were not enough pennies left to cover a week's rent. Roger had to move out, which was not difficult, but the owner of the building let him stay until he got another tenant and then let Roger sleep in the basement in return for doing odd jobs and stoking the fire. Until his clothes should wear out, Roger's basic wants were met.

Lillie's death made a greater and more abrupt change in Roger's life than merely moving from the apartment to the basement. Dependence had gone, and that was something to think about. Any sense of direct personal loss was swallowed up by the horror of disease and death, and he recalled her, haphazardly, as a person who had not been unkind to him. Lillie's earthly immortality was bound to be a mite negative.

Roger soon adjusted to his new kind of freedom. There was no one to account to or to help or to avoid. Instead of seeking companionship with the boys he knew from school, he developed his solitude by withdrawing even from Joe and keeping to himself. He prowled the desolate beaches beyond the rocky outcroppings where his tide pools were, taking his fish or a rabbit and cooking them over driftwood fires. He began to find great contentment in these days and he could even endure the crash of the waves as they lanced obliquely along the tide line and rolled into an apron of slicing white foam. The wet sand was as smooth as sealskin, and the high point of each wave was marked by a tiny ridge of sand freighted in by the last veneer of advancing water. He watched the fading glow of the sun and the coming of night.

He had to learn to cook over a beach fire. Joe had done what little cooking there was before, when they took most of their bag home. Now Roger was alone and he generally burned the few rabbits that he caught, but he learned to burn them less as time went on. Even the blackened fat tasted crisp and good when it stuck to his fingers, and the flesh beneath was tender. The little bodies, cleaned of fur and viscera, were no larger around than his arm or the joints of their legs bigger than his fingers. One rabbit made a meal.

The days grew shorter, but the scrub oak and maple caught fire as autumn drew along, and there was wine in the air. Feet went lightly on the earth and the tonic in nature seemed to match the needs of flesh. Man felt poised above normal, as if he had taken drugs. Even the first hard storms of the dying year had an uplifting quality after the flat and leaden heat of summer.

Roger felt called upon to live. He could not translate the feeling into an awareness of quality, for he was too young to see in the miniature of details the world's whole beauty or feel its call to creative action. He could see only the distant horizon and feel a hunger to eat and sleep and be refreshed. Beyond this there was a vague unease in him, an inability to touch the glowing world or appease directly or fully any hunger that he felt.

Such moods and seasons do not last, and Roger returned to normal as the days withered and the earth and sea grew cold. If he turned again to Joe, he met a new response, a preoccupation with something that Roger felt was nothing like the upland season through which he had just passed. They were reserved with each other and nothing was said. They saw less and less of each other, and Joe's withdrawal was the more deliberate. These were the weeks when he was his sister's lover. He seemed no longer to see Roger, who in turn became preoccupied with the effort to eat and live.

As the cold of winter settled upon the town it seemed to squeeze what little food there was beyond the people's grasp. The soup kitchens opened only sporadically, and the summer jobs like small construction and cutting grass petered out before the advancing frost. Men seemed to hibernate, as if to save what fat they had. There were no rabbits in the fields and woods, and the fish went deeper beyond the sloping beaches, to save themselves from being flung ashore by storms. Nature was silent when there was no wind, and when the bronze of December was in the trees and grasses the earth lay still and slept.

Roger kept warm in his shakedown near the furnace, but he got no food there. He had been underfed since leaving school, but now he was on starvation rations. He grew thin and was continuously hungry and joined the men who slunk like rats to scavenge from garbage pails or from the town dump. Sometimes what he ate sickened and poisoned him, and at times he gagged over half-decayed morsels that he sought to taste and chew. If Joe was in one of his rare good humors, he would see that Roger had first chance at the garbage: his father was working, and from what the family ate the refuse was at least new and reasonably fresh. But Joe's good humor became increasingly rare, until one day he suddenly set upon Roger and beat him savagely. Roger had asked him how his sister was, just to show an interest, and Joe turned on him with a wild light in his eye. After that he kept away from Joe. He did not speculate on the other's odd behavior, for most people were grim and sultry under the burden of how to stay alive. He simply crossed Joe off his small list of reliable people.

The winter also failed to co-operate. A mild season would have allayed a great deal of suffering, but it grew into an abrasive and unbroken spell of cold. During January and February Roger's situation was close to desperate, and he planned to watch for the first break in the weather that might bring back the fish and rabbits. Other men did the same, meeting each other in the woods and passing without a word, pretending not to read each other's thoughts.

It is surprising that Roger now did not steal. The alienist was at once interested in that. He thought that the reasons why people did not commit crimes when they might be expected to—as, for instance, when they later did—were quite as interesting as the reasons why they did commit them. The conventional four h's—hatred, hunger, heart, and home—accounted for many crimes, and very often no further reason existed: a starving man stole because he was hungry. Why Roger did not do so interested the alienist very much, but he got little help from Roger. In fact, the boy seemed surprised by the idea, suggested by the doctor, that a man might steal in the autumn and arrange to be caught in order to ensure a warm cell, with meals, over the winter. All that Roger was sure of was that the thought of jail neither attracted nor deterred him. In fact, he did not even think about it. If a reason could be suggested for him, it might be that his solitary nature kept him from companions, good or bad, and that because his life had always been simple, it was not different enough in degree, when it became hard, to appear to him different in kind. He was unable to analyze his cast of independence, but he had one and it worked.

About the middle of March there came a definite spring thaw. The small ice melted, leaving the large coarse grains in dirty patches in the streets and fields. Roger made it a habit to go regularly to the few places in town that might offer work, and he was passing the schoolhouse one morning when Dr. Beechum turned into the street just behind him and called his name. He was a kind man who remembered his pupils and did small things for them when he could. He did one now, for Roger looked as if he needed it. The principal knew about the death of Roger's aunt, and his eyes told him the rest. He was actually on his way to the local employment office to find a temporary janitor to replace the one that had broken his leg. He looked thoughtfully at Roger.

"Can you stoke a furnace?" he asked.

Roger gave him a swiftly gathering look and told him that he was doing so now in return for a place to sleep.

"You get no pay," Dr. Beechum stated as a fact. Roger agreed that he did not.

"We can't pay much here, as you probably know," he said, "but we need a man to fill in while Stan Howard is laid up, and if you're interested you can have the job."

Roger was never effusive, but a sudden light shone in

his face and his tongue stumbled to accept the offer. So much over so little, the principal said to himself, and told Roger that he had better start at once so the fire wouldn't go out. He was about to offer the boy a bit of his small wages in advance, but something in Roger's face restrained him. He merely smiled a little sadly and turned to re-enter the school. Roger was already on his way to the janitor's door that led to the basement.

He soon familiarized himself with the big furnace. It left him plenty of time for himself, especially in the thawing weather, and he redoubled his efforts to find food. It was only five days to payday, and he found that he drew strength from being able to count on something.

With the ground softening and a warmer wind making a deeper sound in the trees, he took to the fields in search of rabbits, his cunning redoubled by the knowledge that he had a job to protect. It was too early to get any but a stray animal, and he would have got none if he had not happened to hear one screaming in the woods. Sensing that it was wounded and could not get away, he followed the sound and presently came upon it. One of its hind legs had been torn off by the animal's frantic efforts to escape from a huge steel trap with teeth in its jaws. It was designed for larger animals, but had closed on the rabbit's leg, almost severing it, and the rabbit had done the rest. Roger was able to fling himself upon it before it could hobble away and to beat in its head with a stone.

Rain and thaw had left no dry wood in the fields or on the beach, but he had ample fire in the school furnace. He knew from his years as a pupil that it was against the rules to use any part of the building for cooking, but he was desperately hungry. He had had no rabbit for months, and in the evening he would be undisturbed in his basement. He hid the body under his coat and made his way to the school.

His one useful possession was a good knife, and he used it to skin the rabbit. Throwing the hide into the furnace, he took the clinker rake and, balancing the carcass over the end, pushed it carefully across the fire. He squatted on his haunches and began to lower the rake to the point where the meat would cook without burning, when he heard someone enter. Fearful of being caught, he gave such a start that the rabbit fell on the coals and began to burn. It fell just inside the lip of the furnace door where the fire was lowest, and he used the rake to drag a heap of coals over the small blazing body.

He looked up. Angela, Joe's sister, was standing in the entrance and looking at him with a slight smile.

His relief that it was no one in authority made him the more angry at losing the rabbit.

"Damn you!" he shouted at the girl. "What do you want?"

She advanced upon him. It was the second time that day that someone had damned her and it did her no good.

"I saw you," she whispered in her anxiety to make her revenge instant and complete. "You were cooking a rabbit, but it fell in. The bones won't burn, they'll find them. I'll tell on you. It's against the rules."

"What's it to you?" he said. "Get out of here and mind your own business."

"I'll tell," she said again, thrusting out her chin and with her eyes blazing at him. "They'll fire you and you'll lose your job and no one else will give you any work because you broke the rules and were fired! I'll do it! I'll do it!" She stamped her foot.

Her fury made her so ugly that Roger had little doubt that she would do it. He had no idea why she wanted to injure him, but his fear from the immediate danger to his job made him oblivious of her motive. All that he could see was that the horrible girl meant to do him harm. She turned as if to go, but he was quicker and seized her. The action steadied him.

"You won't!" he said in a low dry voice. "I'll keep you here until you say you won't."

He thought for a fleeting moment that it would be a

battle of their two wills and that he would win because
he had the better case. He meant to hold her and shake
her in order to stop her from leaving and prevent her
from talking and making noise. But she was beyond anything rational. In her wild desire to run free and to
avenge herself lay his one possible chance, if he could
have known it. If he had laughed at her and told her
to go ahead and tell and had pushed her out of the door,
she might have started running again and run the specific venom out of her. But she was being held, and the
last thing she could abide was constriction of any kind.
There had been enough of that from Joe. She lost her
head and began to kick at his legs and scratch at his
arms. And she began to scream.

At the dreadful noise Roger lost all control except the
will to stop it. His hands flew from her arms to her
throat. He must squeeze her vocal cords together so she
couldn't scream. If he held them, she could make no
sound because she would have to breathe. He had to
stop the noise that came from her. He must shake her to
bring her to her senses. Squeeze and shake, shake and
squeeze, and when she was quiet he would reason with
her. He didn't feel her hands fluttering at his to pry
them loose. He couldn't hear that he was growling like
an animal. He couldn't see through the red haze of rage
and panic that her eyes were popping and her tongue

swelling out and her face turning blue. He didn't feel the fingers of his two hands meeting and interlocking around her neck until there was only half the thickness of a neck.

All that came through to him was that the screaming sound had ceased. He hadn't heard the few last harsh rattles of her breath. He must shake her by the shoulders now, shake sense back into her. He didn't see that he was shaking her with a terrible violence or feel his tongue half bitten through between his teeth. He couldn't realize that her head was flying wildly back and forth as he shook her. He didn't hear the muffled crack as her neck broke and her body went limp and slumped in his hands. He hardly felt her weight against his frenzied muscles. With lowered head and face set in a hideous grimace, he gave his full and desperate strength to shaking her head back and forth over and over again. Her flying hair swept across his face, and when at last he felt it he let her go. She sank in a heap to the floor, her face hidden. He fell beside her, suddenly weak and panting.

"Take it back!" he said hoarsely. "Take back what you said about telling, and go home!"

He got no answer. He thought that she was crying and put his hand on her shoulder. There was no resistance to his push, and he pushed a little more. She rolled onto her back and he saw her distorted and discolored face. Her eyes glazed over as he looked at them.

For a moment he refused to accept the thought that she was dead. He must have hurt her more than he intended, but people always came to after a while. He moved one of her hands, and it fell limply. A chill went through him, and he felt for her pulse. There was none. His face twisted with fear, he bent his head over her and put his ear to her breast. There was no sound. Slowly, as if his life depended on it, he reached out his hand and put it gently against her face. As he did so he felt it grow cool.

For the second time panic swept over him. Perhaps her screams had been heard before he stopped them. He could not leave her here dead, to be found. He remembered the rabbit and cautiously took the fork and felt for it. All that he could locate was a little ash and some bone. As the thought struck him, he gasped and revolted from it, but in the searing process of great fear he saw that there was nothing else to do. She must follow the rabbit.

His heart was going so fast that he could not distinguish the beats: they were a long, weakening flutter. He could barely move, but he forced himself erect and bent over Angela to lift her. Dragging her under the arms, he pulled himself together for a final effort and forced her head and shoulders foremost through the wide furnace door. At once he could hear the crackle of her burning hair and in a moment caught a whiff of burning flesh. He pushed her in up to her waist and then collapsed on the floor and had to sit there for some time, leaning against the dead girl's buttocks and gasping from the wild threading of his heart. From somewhere deep within him an old memory flashed: "Part of me would stick out!" He heard himself laugh crazily and suddenly realized that he had not eaten for three days. No matter. His hunger must wait. He must dispose of this thing half in and half out of the furnace. He could hear the sizzling and broiling of its face and arms.

He must get a fresh hold on it, weak as he was, and he grasped it around the thighs. It all must have taken him nearly a quarter of an hour. The room was swimming before his eyes, but he meant to get a grip on the body and force it in with his last strength. He grasped it clumsily, and instead of moving ahead the body moved sideways and slipped out of the furnace door. He reached for an arm to gather the body in a new hold. He didn't notice that the arm was smoking. As he touched it he felt a flaming burn. By reflex action the burned fingers flew to his mouth, and he sucked them as a person sucks a burn. Drawing his mouth away, he looked at his hand to see the wound. His fingers were red and blistering, but whole. There was a substance still in his mouth and he found that he was chewing and tasting it—a crisp taste, sweet and tender.

It was his hunger that led him to the last dreadful act. He saw the place on the girl's arm where a bit of her skin and flesh had come away on his fingers. The arm was cooler now, when he touched it to make sure that there was some missing flesh. He saw the arm no longer as an arm but as a piece of cooked meat, blackened and corrugated like many of his rabbits. Slowly and with irresistible curiosity, he raised it to his mouth to taste again the delicious crispness. Horror at what he was doing lay walled off, beaten back by his hunger. As if it had a separate existence, made ravenous by what it had tasted, his mouth moved downward for food, and bit. It was the tenderest of rare meat. At the full taste his hunger flooded over him and he ate as a starving man eats. He seemed to be swimming in a light liquid which sustained him for the one purpose of allaying his tyrannous appetite. He ate savagely along the arm from near the elbow to the wrist, and when he got there he noticed that what was left was a hand. His hunger partly satisfied, the recognition of it as a hand, the skin burst over the knuckles and the fat crisp and brown, brought him back to himself and he saw in a rush of horror what he had done. He staggered to his feet and was violently sick.

When the paroxysms were over, he gazed about him in terror. He could do nothing with the awful mess: the half-eaten arm, the partially burned body, the vomit. There was only one thing left to do, to put it all behind him as far as possible. He groped to the door and began to run.

He was caught the next day, wandering about as if in a trance and not even trying to hide. And as if he were looking for someone to turn to, he babbled forth his story to the detectives. For once he was not reserved, and all they had to do to persuade him was to feed him. It might have been significant, had they noticed it, as the psychiatrist did later, that he did not mention a sexual attack on Angela.

Even without his statement there was little doubt of what he had done. The girl's flesh was in his vomit. He had abandoned both of his jobs and was missing. Angela's body was submitted to the coroner's physician for autopsy, and among the report of bruises, strangulation marks, a broken neck, and a partly eaten arm, there appeared the terse statement: "Male sperm was found in the uterus."

Roger was arrested and duly indicted for first-degree murder and rape. For good measure, in order that the whole fearful story should get before the jury, there was added an indictment for the common-law misde-

meanor of mutilating a dead body by eating a portion
of it, to wit, an arm. This, the District Attorney said sen-
tentiously to the newspapers, was cannibalism.

All right-thinking people condemned Roger as a monster and a sex fiend, and since there was no ready syno-
nym for cannibal, which soon became overworked, he
was called a Vampire and a Devil's Communicant. The
press printed smashing editorials and withering inter-
views with learned men and righteously pointed to the
Causes of Crime. No one knew what they were, exactly,
but they were something about which something must
be done, and the extermination of Roger seemed to be
the first step. The Chief of Police, who made the most of
capturing Roger, issued a statement calling for a speedy
trial to vindicate the fair name of Justice. Women, wishing that they could be more devoured than they were
by some man's affection, said that the electric chair was
too good for the little demon. There were some who suggested, with a strange glitter in their eyes, that the un-
speakable young beast had violated the girl's body after
death. They even knew the word for it: necrophilia.

Old Judge Parkinsen was assigned to preside at the
trial. He declared, and was quoted, that he would sit
day and night to bring the young miscreant to book. He
hastily had to issue a rider in the next edition that of

course the defendant's legal rights would be scrupulously protected. What it meant was that Judge Parkinsen intended to murder him.

There is a Judge Parkinsen in every legal community, a man of outward judicial demeanor but with a head full of sawdust and the soul of a man-eating shark. The community gets him because it deserves him: the ablest lawyers cannot be bothered to accept judicial duty, and the method of selecting judges is predominantly political.

Judge Ulen was doing his monthly stint in Miscellaneous Court when Roger was brought up for arraignment. Ulen could not abide Judge Parkinsen and needed to know no more about the case than that Parkinsen was on the war-path. He had read the newspapers with misgiving and now looked at Roger with interest. The boy seemed almost cheerful. At seventeen and a half, he had no feeling that he was in any real danger, and he had, in a way, never had life so pleasant. People came to interview him, and he ate regularly and was warm.

Ulen explained to him that he would have to appoint counsel since Roger had no money to afford one of his own, and continued the case for a week.

When he returned to his chambers he had the pleasant surprise of finding Artema Longa waiting for him. She had once been his secretary, but had left him when she married. She came only rarely to see him and usually with a reason, so he lifted his eyebrows inquiringly as they shook hands. If he had the glimmer of an idea, it was not his turn to disclose it, so he stuffed his pipe and said: "What on earth?"

"You should know," she said. "Roger Haike."

"Yes, there's Roger," he replied. "The witch-fires are alight on all the hills and the death drums are throbbing. The trial will be the auto-da-fé of the century in these parts, and I need someone to represent him who will stand up. Any volunteers?"

"Of course. My modest Morris wouldn't come and lay his head on the block, but he burst out to me and here I am."

"It will be tough," said Ulen, thinking aloud. "It will be tough unless he pleads Roger guilty, and that means ushering him straight into the electric chair. But Morris will know what to do if he can do it."

"He's already done it," said Artema primly. "He knows a young doctor who is trying to become an alienist. Morris was talking with him about the case and he said the crime is so frightful that the boy must be sick or crazy. Morris knows he's interested. He'll do it with or without pay."

Ulen sat back with a sigh. "He's in for a rough time," he remarked, "but bless him. Tell Morris he's a great guy and I'll appoint him, but I can't promise that Parkinsen will allow a medical fee as part of the costs. I fear it would be like him not to."

And so it was that a week later Morris Longa, Esquire, was appointed to represent Roger. He went doubtfully to the prison for his first interview with his new client, but found the job of winning his confidence easier than he had expected. Morris, at fifty, had lived life hard before he married Artema and had emerged with compassion and his native abilities at their peak. Roger looked at his lined face and felt a friendly and patient lack of prejudice there. His mood of cheerfulness when he first appeared before Judge Ulen had considerably subsided. Less attention was now paid him, and as the days went on he felt the bleak outlines of the case pressing in upon him.

When Morris entered his cell he looked up eagerly. A memory from his childhood made him cry out: "Are you going to take care of me?"

Morris said that he would do his best, and in a few minutes the boy was pouring out his story. Morris gently led him on, and as he listened his heart turned over and sank. It wasn't the kind of story any jury would believe, under the circumstances. That he believed it only added to his pain. Yes, he would try indeed.

Roger knew the outlines of the case against him and knew that it was dangerous, but with the inexperience of youth he felt that his lawyer could work magic. Grown-ups rarely bothered about kids, but when they did they had the strength to beat down any opposition. All they had to do was try, because other grown-ups were always preoccupied and would pay only half-attention. He felt that Morris would try, and he would try too, and together nothing could stand against them, for they would catch the other grown-ups off balance. There would be a hard fight and a glorious victory, and he would have new friends and a real place in the community. It was too early to feel remorse.

Morris felt the boy's trust, and Artema read the pain in his haggard face when he came home. "There isn't a chance," he told her. "Not a real chance. He denied the rape and seems honestly bewildered that they should think such a thing of him. I had to tell him what is in the coroner's report, and he kept repeating: 'But it wasn't mine.' He says he only meant to keep her quiet and not to choke her. He thought she would wake up. He admits he ate some of her, the smell of roasting meat was too much for him. My God, how can you beat a thing like that, even if he hadn't eaten in three days and had been half starved for years? The hungry people on the jury probably never ate anybody, and that's what will kill Roger. And he confessed it to the police, the same story he told me. They'll murder him, but there's just a chance that I can make the jury think that no one could eat human flesh unless he was crazy. It's the only chance there is. I wish he was crazy now, but he isn't."

When Roger next appeared before Ulen he pleaded not guilty by reason of insanity and was assigned to a jury trial at the pleasure of the State.

The District Attorney, Henry Moulder, announced that he himself would try the case and continued prosecuting Roger in the newspapers. And the papers were happy to oblige, since this sort of thing was considered news. Morris moved to quash the indictment for cannibalism on the ground that it was no offense in law because no penalty attached to it. Parkinsen brusquely overruled him. Morris then moved to change the venue and hold the trial in a distant County. He was again overruled, but he had a nice record of affidavits and editorials and news stories to show the impossibility of an impartial trial.

The battle lines were drawn.

Comment

LET US NOT be shocked by the idea that man can eat his fellow.

It is close under the surface of our minds, as murder is. Take a year's sheaf of cartoons from newspapers and magazines and see the scores of cannibalistic situations, from gentle professors standing in hot cauldrons amid dancing savages to giants threatening to eat up small but heroic boys.

It is sublimated reverently into profound religious experience in our Church Communion.

What happens in the corners and byways of our familiar world? In the thousands of dissecting-rooms, embalming-parlors, hospitals, and medical schools? Surely the cold and thrusting scientific mind, born into the family of carnivorous man who slaughters and eats tens of thousands of birds and fish and beasts every year, would be tempted and would yield to the experiment of tasting human meat. Is there never curiosity so alert that it does not venture the cooking of a small mortal filet over an alcohol burner, just to see?

One of the earliest legends of the Western world concerns Zeus, son of Chronos and Rhea. It was prophesied by Uranus and Gaia that Chronos would be deposed by one of his own children. Chronos tried to avert this fate by swallowing each baby born to his wife, Rhea, and he did eat the first five. Pregnant with her sixth, Rhea fled to Crete and in a mountain cave gave birth to Zeus, king of the Grecian gods. Returning to her husband, Rhea presented him with a stone dressed as a baby, and Chronos swallowed it.

Daily we eat our neighbors in spirit or in mind, by cruelty and domination and the crushing jaws of an imperious will.

Let us not be so squeamish about the violence of the body when we are so very tolerant of the violence of the mind.

The purpose of this book is to show what happened to Roger Haike and to protest against it.

And also to protest against a criminal and penal system that is founded on vengeance. Punishment as a concept is the bad thing, and capital punishment is only the most dramatic form of punishment. The penology of the future is treatment, not to fit the crime but to fit the prisoner. Someday we will look back upon our criminal and penal process with the same horrified wonder as we now look back upon the Spanish Inquisition.

A judge is tempted to feel the hot hatred of the chase, and even if he can steel himself against it he still knows that he is rendering public vengeance. The process is to pursue and catch and flay, and it is the old story of man's inhumanity to man.

Sitting in the universal chair of observation, we know what Roger did and what was in his mind and heart. We know that he was innocent of rape and guilty of no degree of homicide higher than second-degree murder, since he had no specific intent to kill Angela. And he was guilty, because he was so devastatingly hungry, of an old common-law misdemeanor. It was not a felony, and it was not even called cannibalism. It was lumped with any offense the gist of which was mutilation of the dead. The District Attorney called it cannibalism in order to make the trial more lurid, the first step in a torrent of self-satisfying horror and perhaps the next rung on the ladder of political promotion.

Nothing of which Roger was guilty carried or deserved the death penalty.

The community, however, settled down to eat the fine raw meat of vengeance. It used the word Justice, but never the word Truth. That was well known: the facts were clear, and truth was not in issue. All that was needed was to watch the process of Justice seat Roger in the electric chair and properly tie him in, and there was great drama even in that, for he would certainly try to wriggle loose. The Courts are still good theater.

In 1931, when the person here called Roger Haike was tried, there was only just beginning to creep into the law of trial procedure and evidence the idea that motive, intention, and the lexicon of psychiatric impulse are relevant. The psychiatrist, or alienist, as he was called then, was just beginning to demand the right to be heard. A few years later the Welfare State came into being and hurried the process: with social security, guaranteed bank deposits, old-age benefits, unemployment compensation, and the like, a new light began to shine on what was hitherto accepted as cold economic fact. Facts no longer seemed unchangeable and stubborn. Something lay behind them that gave them a new aspect.

The law usually requires motive to inculpate. That is,

there must be criminal intent, or *mens rea,* before a man can be convicted. What his intention may be is judged by his acts, without explanation. In some crimes, such as carrying a concealed deadly weapon, the law provides that the intent to do harm with the weapon may be inferred by the fact-finder from the circumstance that the defendant was carrying the weapon concealed. In a large class of cases known as offenses under the police power, intent counts for nothing, and a man who does not know that someone put a case of untaxed liquor in his car can see both car and liquor confiscated and have no redress. If a man takes a short lobster, it makes no difference that his measure was faulty and that he thought it was a legal lobster: he is subject to fine. This class of offense is growing larger.

But no exculpatory motive is relevant. Everyone is presumed to know the law, and we know quite well that no one knows it all. His knowledge being unprovable as a fact, the law supplies it in the form of the presumption just mentioned, and hence no man will be heard to say that he did not know that his action was criminal. If he knew what he was doing, it makes no difference that he did not know that it was specifically wrong. We rely on human experience to bridge the gap. Human beings can be expected generally to know what constitutes murder, robbery, rape, burglary, and the like, and to know that such things are wrong. Only mental blank or insanity will excuse them.

The drive behind a man's act has so far been held to be irrelevant. Society has had to adopt this stand as a principle of law because without it confusion would have been worse confounded. No one has well understood the subconscious powers of the mind or the direction of its dark paths. Without informed advice, every assertion of irresistible impulse would on the surface require acquittal.

The psychiatrist is gaining ground, but his greatest difficulty is that we are a fact-loving people. Facts guide and govern our science and our industrial economy, and those who mistrust facts are the artists, the ministers, the philosophers, the teachers, and some judges.

Hence it became Fact in the small seacoast city that Roger Haike had tried to dispose of Angela's body after he had raped her and then killed her to prevent her from telling on him. And what sealed the status of it all as Fact was the one thing that had nothing to do with what had gone before—the grisly eating of her arm. Anyone who did such things should die. The trial was required only to establish the obvious.

The dreadful truth is that there are more innocent people convicted than there are guilty people acquitted. There is no doubt of this when we include people who are guilty of something but are convicted of something else, and when the forfeit is life or liberty they have a right not to appreciate poetic justice. A scientific and factual nation should specify accurately. When a man is jailed for what he did not do, he knows that he was not jailed for what he did do. Neither result is fair, to him or to the public.

It is better to talk about what is fact and what is fair than it is to prate about Truth and Justice. No one knows what those great but slippery words mean. If they have pragmatic value, it may be said that Truth is what people take with them to Court. Justice is what they take away with them, and it may be good or bad or indifferent, but it is all justice. In between it is not the law but the process of the law, the kinetic flowing stream of fact and precept, that sends men to prison or to their death. Hence the enormous importance of due process.

There are certain things that can be said about the monumental words.

We know that truth is the thing that makes men lie.

We can probably agree with Holmes that the truth is what we cannot help thinking, and that it is not necessarily cosmic: the reasons for thinking it utterly may be good or bad.

Truth is not static. What is truth when we are very

angry? Are we not convinced that the hard and holy truth is raging red-hot within us? What is truth when we are very frightened? Does not every fact of life, however usually benign, seem fraught with menace? What, when we are cool and calm? It is surely not the same in all three cases. In fright or anger truth is not accurate and objective fact but sheer intensity of feeling: passion itself becomes truth. Aristotle has said that nothing beyond the speech of common mortals can be spoken save by the agitated soul. There is room for truth that is feeling and not fact.

A confession appears to be a clear form of proven truth, but nothing could be farther from the purpose. Some confessions are beaten out of prisoners, who say anything to end the torture: the third degree, physical or mental, is not yet dead among us. A confessor may try to protect a friend or to hide a deeper truth than the one that he acknowledges. He may confess in order to bring masochistic punishment upon himself. It does not follow that the community should always agree with a confessor's sense of guilt.

We can stand only a little truth, no more than what the average man is able to bear and walk around with. That is the universal level of the law, the average conduct of the average man. Hence the lawyer's commodity is not truth but credibility, the measure of likelihood, the norm by which a man can safely consent to be measured, the broad reliable path cut through the actual history of the race. It is part good, part evil, part falsehood, part truehood. If we understand the difference between truth and credibility, we will understand the difference between law and procedure. The one must deal with fact while the other, the kinetic flowing stream, allows for illusion. It must not be forgotten that a trial is a reconstruction of past acts and that there is bound to be refraction. If the procedures are kept clean and vital, the refraction is kept down and the struggle of the law to become truth can go forward.

The next step is that the law become custom, a man's voluntary obedience to the unenforceable. That is far ahead in the future of the race.

And what of Justice?

It is usually another name for winning one's case. The shout "Justice has triumphed!" means that the verdict has gone the shouter's way.

Or it is given an initial capital letter and ponderous encomiums are paid to it. There is more puppetry and posturing about Justice and Judges than in any other field of our national life, but it has an honest base. In a nation that calls its Chief Executive by a nickname, no judge is ever so addressed, save by his intimates. A judge wields direct power over his neighbors, and hence there is fear in their submission, but there is respect as well for the impartial mind, which is rare enough. Brains have always been suspect, but a man well paid to walk the narrow pathway of the law and treat his fellows evenly is a fit subject of veneration, and judges get it whether they deserve it or not. It is a little saddening, such trust, and yet needful.

Capitalized, Justice is apt to become a system. This is inevitable to a degree, for when organized by the law and moved along by legal procedure, results are had— a proper enough definition of a system. So long as it is tied to the concept of the average behavior of the average man, least harm is done. Our justice does not apply the standards of the few to the actions of the many, but average standards, and hence achieves a workable compromise between the individual and the crowd.

Compare this with the ideal of honor capitalized into Honor and once made into a system of artificial aphorisms called the *code duello*. It was thought that what was honorable could be codified and made a vital department of conduct. What happened was that the woods filled with the dead and wounded bodies of variously honorable men. The code was harsh, not vital, for no man's ideal is quite another's, and no one profited save the system. If a man is not judged by his own ideal, subject to the known pressures upon him, no intelligent sanction can be selected or applied. If we let our ideals escape into systems, we are moving toward that dangerous area where a thing and the name of a thing get mixed up.

Our law and justice are constantly being saved from the worst of that confusion because cases consist of single people and their doings. We cannot get far from the average norm, since the solitary human being is at the base of civil liberty and due process. For whom else could these great protections exist?

We can codify our law but not our justice. But perhaps we do worse. Justice should be the little side chapel where the mysteries and the miracles of the stolid law take place. How dreadful to show her powers crippled by a blindfold and her hands encumbered by sword and scale! She should be free to look far and deep into people, and to bring healing in her hands. Not the Blind Goddess but the Angel Who Attends To Things.

At the bottom of these questions is the basic one of what to do with a fact. No longer can these difficult things stand revealed but unexplained. Freud has set a great wind blowing in man's mind, and the dark flowers that grow there are swaying before it, needing to be gathered and understood. Instead of the law's presumption that a man is sane, psychiatry insists that all men must conclusively be presumed to be a little mad. In the law this is a tough cross-wind, and it is driving the profession to regard facts as icebergs, complete with large underbodies which must be examined. And the growth of the Welfare State is setting the stage for a new dimension in treating criminals.

The profession will soon have to do basic research in the problems of fact-finding, especially in the criminal field, where men are not being held accountable for the same things or for the same reasons as once they were. There may be less need on the civil side of the law, where the rules of property are the rules of the game and, *stare decisis*, have been for a long time. Unless society, as distinct from the law, changes its rules about property, the present ones will do. This is not so in matters of personal freedom, and unless reforms are carried forward, people will not put up with a system that has proven itself outworn. The usual signs of unrest are prison breaks and riots, which already sweep the country from time to time. Prisoners are people.

It is necessary not to make a fetish of the notion that law is logical. It may be logical or illogical, as best suits its purpose at the moment. The unfounded statement that everyone knows the law is obviously absurd and yet is a necessary presumption if the law is to operate uniformly and smoothly. Another presumption, of great age, is the homely idea that husband and wife are one person. But if he commits a crime and is put in jail for it, she is not put there too on the theory that they are one flesh. She goes back to support the children in the home that no creditor of either may reach because it is in their joint names. It is good public policy that the law should be illogical in the one case and logical in the other, concerning the same two people.

A fine aphorism is Lord Coke's about the beauty of the law being the known certainty thereof. If this is so, then large fields of the law are singularly unlovely. To mention one, there is the case of the two-year-old infant who is killed in an automobile collision. The jury must not only be allowed but required to guess a whole lifeful of factors and damages. Nothing could be less certain than such necromancy.

A final example of legal logic is the story, familiar to lawyers, about the hole in a London street which had grown to dangerous proportions. The authorities decided to notify the owner to fix it. But by one of those odd chances that seem to occur only in England, a small section of the street in which the hole was located had no owner and had never had one. Whom to serve? The Sheriff's solicitor finally and rather brilliantly concluded that if no one owned the hole, at least the hole must own itself. Armed with process, therefore, a bailiff went out and made known to the hole that it should appear be-

fore the Court on a certain date and there give cause,
if any it had, etc., or judgment. On the appointed day
the case was called before three judges in wigs, but the
hole failed to appear. Three times it was called, and in
the corridor as well, but there was no answer, while Justice waited. Absence being established, judgment was
given against the hole, and the municipal authorities
went out and filled it up. Most great ideas are dramatic
or amusing at their extreme ends: while British justice
waited in the case of Regina *v.* One Hole in Blank
Street, there waited also the whole history of English
civil liberty and due process of law.

No one need be concerned with logic when it comes
to reforming the law. It is a very human and not a very
scientific institution. Average standards of conduct are
more important, and the pressures and motives of the
single person are becoming more important yet.

We must not forget him. Specifically, we must not forget Roger Haike. As we go on with the story of truth
and justice as he found them, we might remember Carl
Sandburg's form of oath and a witness's reply:

*"Do you solemnly swear before the everliving
God that the testimony you are about to give in
this cause shall be the truth, the whole truth, and
nothing but the truth?"*

*"No, I don't. I can tell you what I saw and what
I heard, and I'll swear to that by the everliving
God, but the more I study about it the more sure I
am that nobody but the everliving God knows the
whole truth, and if you summoned Christ as a witness in this case, what He would tell you would
burn your insides with the pity and the mystery
of it."*

II

The Trial

ROGER HAIKE went to trial in the early summer of 1931.

All of the important events of his life, excepting only his graduation and his solitude in the woods and on the beach, had occurred in mean and ugly places. The scene of his trial was no exception. Even by the end of the fruitful years before the depression modern architecture had not overtaken courthouses and courtrooms. They were uniformly square and hard, without softening of line or sense of sculptured space which came later with a more imaginative age. The courthouse where Roger's trial took place was of gray limestone long since gone grimy in the city air. One mounted worn steps, walked in upon worn floors, and turned hard right to enter the worn courtroom. Its high square windows rattled in the wind and leaked in cold weather. The ancient radiators, whose pipes banged dismally and without warning, filled the room with rising hot air through which the settling cold air created odd layers of chill and heat. The hot air was dry and felt almost as hard as the floor in its impact against lips and nostrils. In warm weather the reflected heat flowed into the open windows from the street, since the courtroom was only half a storey above ground level, and fans whined and circled, spraying the dead air from one part of the room to another.

The floor of the courtroom was hardwood, worn down to splinters in which shreds from the cleaning-women's mops had caught and stuck. The worst sections had been covered with linoleum, whose holes had in turn been patched. A constant whisper of scuffing shoes was heard when the room was full, and a creaking of the false-maple chairs whose sprung joints made them sway ominously when people shifted their positions. The bar had suffered numerous coats of varnish to change its color and increase its thickness. The same was true of the bench, on whose extreme ends short pillar lamps rose to a round white globe which shone blindingly at night sessions of Court. The judge sat on a cane swivel chair permanently tilted rearward from long use, and some physical exertion was needed to bring His Honor upright. This chair rested on a crude mosaic of small marble squares, badly chipped, showing a white center with a narrow red rim as its only design. The castors had been removed because they tended to roll on the mosaic, and a judge, wool-gathering during a futile cross-examination, might roll altogether off the bench. Without its castors the chair was difficult to pull forward or push backward when the Court sat and later rose, but it occurred to no one to change it or anything else in the room.

Naked bulbs set in ancient gas fixtures which had been transformed into electric-light brackets provided illumination. It was usually needed on gray days, since half of the window space was covered with thick dark-green velour curtains waisted back with once-golden cord now tarnished black. People leaning too heavily against them caused thin clouds of dust to rise lazily. A space walled off by wooden barriers and containing twelve stiff chairs was the jury box, beyond one corner of the bench. Between was the witness stand, a miniature jury box with one chair. The door leading to the cellroom and beyond it to the house of detention was behind the witness chair.

The room seemed heavy, as if with the psychic deposit from thousands of feet and bottoms of people who had witnessed the tragedy, the comedy, and the monotony of an ordinary trial Court. This and countless others like it throughout the nation were once the country's principal theater. Here wit and learning and bombast were free for all to hear, and the crowds came eagerly to see if the caught fox could escape. Because of the refraction of time between the event and its reconstruction at trial, the populace might feel very differently about crimes and criminals in the street and in Court. What was once a dastardly act later became a fine wrestling match, with sympathy usually for the culprit who tried to beat back the organized shock troops of society.

A Court is still good theater, despite the stage and cinema and television, all of which must again refract by having to set a trial within a restricted frame of time. In Court the actors are alive, the stakes are high and real, and a full chapter of justice can be seen, complete in time and space and inference. Pressure of work has shortened trials greatly, especially in the cities, but there is still room for illusion and for the drama of the chase.

Roger Haike, fiend incarnate, was offering a double bill. He was going to say that his mind had forsaken him, and all right-thinking people knew how absurd that was: the destruction of such a flimsy defense would be the curtain-raiser. The real show would be the destruction of Roger. It was a pity the State had gone soft by substituting the electric chair for hanging. Stretching his neck a foot would be about right for him.

Spring brings its blessings even into prisons. Roger felt the earth slacken and could see the narrow world that his single barred window revealed to him grow soft and green. April, as one poet has put it, was gowned in blue and silver air, and it lifted Roger's spirit with comfort. In such a world, for all its bars, nothing could go very seriously wrong: one must live out the battle and at evening always come home. It was as if people put on costumes and acted in plays of varying severity, but they took them off at dusk and nothing that had happened in the play meant anything. The only reality was the warmth of home, and to Roger, who knew little of what a home could be like beyond bed and kitchen, it meant the attitude of people and the things they would or would not do to him. No one had ever done him much harm, except that girl. Now he had an abode of a sort, with warmth and regular food.

Dr. Danby had no easy time with him. It was not that he was hostile, as he would have been if he had not had confidence in Morris. The lawyer had tried to explain before Dr. Danby first talked with him.

"We must face what's against us," he said. "I can't

make it any easier than it is, and it's pretty bad. They think you raped her, killed her, and ate her, and they can prove it all. The fact that you didn't rape her and didn't intend to kill her doesn't count. It's the eating that will prevent their believing you."

Roger shuddered. "I don't know why—why I did that," he said. "I hardly remember anything until—"

"Yes, you told me how hungry you were," Morris interrupted. "That's our chance, if we can make the jury believe that you did it because you were frightened and angry and starving, and that the effect of all three things was to make you temporarily insane. You must help. I can't do it alone. You must talk to Dr. Danby and tell him everything he wants to know, no matter how personal or unpleasant it is."

There was no need to say more, for Roger knew what would happen to him if the jury did not believe them, even if he was as yet unable to accept it as possible. But many people have been hanged or imprisoned because they failed to express themselves well, and Roger was sparse of words. The habit of saying little made it almost impossible now to say anything that normally would have been left unsaid.

Dr. Danby persevered. He was a young man and he was upset by Roger's predicament. Like many earnest and kindly young men, he felt that an underdog deserved special support, even if it failed to meet all the niceties of his difficult professional oath. He was in a fight which he had not begun and which the adversary, who was the District Attorney, was conducting most unfairly in the public press. Danby figuratively rolled up his sleeves and waded in. When Roger proved unwilling or incapable of revealing a particularly hard knot in himself, Danby hypnotized him, got what he wanted, woke Roger up, and told him what he had said. It was then not difficult for Roger to accept what he was told he had said and soon to say it again in his own words. Danby, at full crusader's gallop, remained shrewd enough to feel it unnecessary to tell Morris that he was doing this, and technically it was no falsehood to report to Morris all that the boy had told him. A life, after all, was at stake. As a matter of fact, there was no need to hypnotize Roger very often. Not only might it prove dangerous if the boy were to realize that he had been put to sleep and to say so in his testimony, but for the most part it was easy enough to lead him a little by putting in better words and perhaps in more fully rounded thought the short, spare sentences of which Roger, even at his most communicative, was capable. Morris thought the campaign was going very well. Dr. Danby was not so sure: he was afraid that Roger might forget some of the best bits, since his recollection of them was somewhat synthetic. Both men told him that he was doing fine.

It was an agonizing season for Morris, who had no illusions about the case, but he was old enough to be at his wiliest and most dangerous when he had a lost cause. He knew what the experienced and most able criminal lawyers know, that the criminal process is the last thing to be sentimental about. It is imperfect enough as it is: hence if it is to be adversary, then let it be adversary. No good-natured agreements or easygoing stipulations. Within the rules, let the State prove a man guilty if it can, without help or quarter. To defend a criminal case with cold and implacable fury has always got the best results. The jury resents the prosecutor who is a persecutor, but it forgives much in a lawyer who fights relentlessly to get his man off under the rules. It was Morris's method, and it had paid. There are enough cases that lose themselves, no matter what a man can do.

The State retained Dr. James McGruder, a veteran of the courts, to study the case and testify. Morris felt exultant. When Moulder called him and asked leave to have Dr. McGruder examine Roger, Morris curtly refused, and Moulder had no alternative but to hang up the phone with a bang, which he did. Now Morris knew when McGruder entered the case, and he could ask him

at the trial whether he had seen or had treated Roger
during the intervening time. Moulder would say that
Morris knew very well that McGruder had not because
he had refused him access to his client. Morris would
then be entitled to instructions, even from a reluctant
Parkinsen, that the defendant had the right to refuse because he could not be compelled to give evidence
against himself, and McGruder would be limited to testifying to what impression he could get of Roger in
Court, while on the stand, or to a hypothetical question
if Roger could safely be kept from testifying. The stage
was as well set as it could be to water down the coun-
terattack on Danby.

"Footwork," he said crossly to Artema. "It doesn't
touch the real issue, but at times it does win cases. The
best McGruder can say now is that not Roger but a boy
in Roger's position, several months ago, knew that what
he was doing was wrong."

The process of condensing years of psychiatric material into three months was wearing. When Morris was
notified of the date set for trial he promptly requested a
postponement, which was promptly denied. The forces
of concentration, frustration, and perplexity were all at
work on Roger, but the denied postponement of the trial

gave Danby some measure of excuse for his unorthodox methods, not only to get the necessary material in time but to lessen the strain on his young patient. Roger began to feel encouraged as the useful responses seemed to come more easily, but he was unearthing things in himself that were not necessary for him to know or appreciate at his age, and hence he was achieving a false overlay of maturity. This may have been protective rather than harmful, with all that he had to meet so quickly and so soon. His face was longer and more settled, but the veneer lay lightly on his belief that the trial was a play that could not be for keeps.

It is hard to say which would have been the better entrance into the crowded courtroom on the first day of the trial: as a frightened, immature youth or as a quiet and self-possessed young man. He was not quite either one when the cellroom door was opened and he was motioned through it by the warder. Morris had got him to dress in a suit of old clothes a bit too big for him, wanting him, without making him self-conscious by telling him, to look as small and abject as possible.

It took them nearly three days to select a jury. Morris's ideal of a favorable juror was an unemployed old man: he wanted no women or restless, able-bodied young men. He used his whole bag of tricks. He had to talk at some length with each juror, to get a reliable impression. Appearances were misleading: many a gentle answer came from a stony face, and vice versa. He had to walk a delicate line between the risk of irritating individual jurors by a long and searching inquiry into the propriety of their serving and the advantage of having hours during which the panel would sit there and watch Parkinsen pick on him. He encouraged the judge to do so, but Parkinsen was an old campaigner too and, except for some marginal sharpness and a general air of weariness, he gave Morris little ground to cry prejudice on appeal. Once Morris accepted a juror who admitted that he had read about the case, hoping that the juror's assertion of inevitable bias from reading such inflammatory articles might cause him to lean over backward to apply his bias to the State. He forced Moulder, who thought that he could rely on his newspaper campaign to produce a favorable jury and wanted to select one quickly, to take time in face of Morris's long colloquies, in order not to appear careless. Moulder was clever about it, asking questions that Morris would have to ask. Once he said:

"Are you sure that you could give this defendant a fair trial?" He paused, leering. "Even if you knew that he was charged, among other things, with cannibalism?"

Morris leaped up with an objection, but Moulder cut him short. "I withdraw the word, Your Honor. The precise charge is 'the mutilation of a dead body by eating a portion thereof, to wit, an arm.' "

The only way Morris could even this out was by asking if the juror would be more likely to impose the death penalty, knowing the charge to be what it was.

The jury as finally chosen consisted of three women and nine men. The average age appeared to be a little over middle age, but an elderly unemployed man balanced the last one chosen, a young unemployed one. It was a hard jury to select, community feeling being what it was, and Morris had used all of his peremptory challenges before two of the women and the young man had been selected. Then having to take whoever came, he had to be content.

The trial began. The audience, restless during the monotonous questioning of the jurors, grew taut. Only those had been admitted to the courtroom who could be seated. The spectators at a trial can be a useful sounding-board, especially for counsel, for aside from having to keep quiet they have no idea that they are an actual part of the dynamics of the proceedings.

In view of his defense of temporary insanity, Morris offered little opposition to the State's case, which went quickly and took only a little over two hours. The facts were all too clear and he had no wish to draw undue attention to them by needless cross-examination. And he might get a little credit from the jury by not fighting senselessly.

He cross-examined the coroner's physician briefly.

"Did you examine the private parts of Angela Hake?" he asked.

"I did."

"Were there any bruises or inflammation at or near them?"

"There were none."

"What can you tell us about the vaginal tract itself?"

"There was an old and completely healed tear in the hymen."

"And what does that signify with regard to sexual intercourse?"

"That normal intercourse can be had with ease."

"Thank you, Doctor, that is all."

The only other witness he paused over was Joe.

It was known that the two boys had been companions, and Moulder put Joe on the stand to show that Roger had a sudden and unreasonable temper. Morris had not spoken to his client about Joe before the trial beyond asking him if he knew the boy. He had no way of knowing that Joe held the key to the charge of rape, and Joe took the stand confidently, knowing that he was safe: he and his sister had never been discovered.

He testified to Roger's attack on him when he began to divide Roger's first rabbit. Not having heard of that before, Morris turned to him for comment.

"Yeah," Roger said in his ear, "that's right, but he once beat me up too, for no reason. All I did was ask how his sister was."

Morris sat for a moment, brooding. Moulder had turned Joe over to him for cross-examination.

"Didn't you once attack him too, when all he did was to ask about your sister?"

A flame of fear shot up in Joe, and its reaction did not escape Morris. "I did not," he said belligerently, and suddenly added: "He hardly knew her."

While Joe's afterthought was unwittingly helpful, Morris felt danger all around him. He did not dare to develop too far the idea of how well Roger had known Angela: Moulder would make the most of what was in the case already. He turned again.

"That's right," Roger whispered. "Only saw her a few times when I went to his house with Joe."

Morris looked at Joe reflectively, and Joe looked back arrogantly. There was something there, but what? A sixth sense told him that beneath his unnecessary arrogance Joe was uneasy. Then it struck him.

In the same blinding flash of realization came the knowledge that he could never use what he had divined.

The boy must know that there was no proof. He would deny it, and if he flinched it would seem to be only horror at being asked such a thing. But, worst of all, Morris knew that he would forfeit whatever shred of sympathy the jury had for Roger if he asked whether Joe had had incestuous relations with his sister. It would be gambling with Roger's life. He pursed his lips tight and shot a hard glance at Joe.

"I have no further questions," he said slowly.

He saw that it was a mistake to ask Joe about his attack on Roger. Joe had denied it, but Moulder might try to ask Roger about it in cross-examination and later argue to the jury that Joe had tried to protect his sister's honor by knocking her defiler down. In view of Joe's denial, this should be improper, but Moulder could be counted on to do anything to counteract the coroner's physician's helpful testimony about Angela's well-worn vaginal tract, and Parkinsen was weak and unpredictable. Moulder would also try to give the jury the impression that Roger had deflowered the girl long before he killed her. It was one of those pieces of bad luck that can happen in a trial.

The State rested at about three o'clock in the afternoon, and Morris, professing himself to be caught unattended by his main witness because of the State's speed in presenting its case, asked for adjournment until morning. Parkinsen demurred at first, wanting to sit through the evening, but it occurred to him that this was a good time to begin granting Morris anything, within reason, that he wanted. Then it could not be said that he had been unfair. He knew Morris would not ask or object unfairly. If he did, he could safely be over-ruled. But so long as Morris invoked the rules, Parkinsen would sustain him.

Many judges do this when they feel sure that the lawyer so favored will be the loser: he will have no ground on which successfully to appeal, if the rulings have gone his way.

Parkinsen did not doubt the outcome, for the facts were stark and horrible. Moulder could not lose this one, and Parkinsen began to favor Morris, who now wanted the impact of Dr. Danby's testimony to come in the morning, when everyone was fresh.

"The motion is granted," said Parkinsen, and Court adjourned.

"Dr. Danby," Morris was asking, after he had briefly addressed the jury, "as a result of examining this boy, and assuming the truth of the facts surrounding the crime as I have just stated them, do you have an opinion about whether or not on the evening of March 3 he knew the difference between right and wrong and knew that what he was doing was wrong?"

"I do," said Danby.

"What is your opinion?"

Moulder objected. He did so not because the question was improper: Morris had carefully included all of the facts in his hypothetical question and it had no other possible legal fault. But Moulder had to play his public and appear to fight at strategic moments. Otherwise he would seem dilatory or defeatist to a lay audience that did not know the ground rules.

"I object," he repeated. "Every man is presumed sane."

"Until the contrary appears," Morris replied dryly. "And to make the contrary appear is the purpose of the question."

Parkinsen had to overrule Moulder. "The contrary must appear by a preponderance of the evidence," he said. "Objection overruled." The words would read flat and legally correct to the Appellate Court, for the stenographic notes could not reflect a raised eyebrow or an accent of sarcasm. One or two of the jurors smiled grimly.

"Proceed, Doctor," Morris said, "and use lay terms so far as possible. Give your opinion first and then explain."

"My opinion is," Danby said clearly, "that on the evening of March 3 Roger Haike did not know the difference between right and wrong and did not know that what he was doing was wrong."

Several of the jurors were gazing at him sullenly. The rest stared ahead of them.

"It may seem strange to you," he went on, "that a man could push a girl's body into a furnace and later eat a part of her without knowing it was wrong to do so.

"Let us go back to his confession. It is an unusual confession because he was asked if he knew that he had done wrong, and he said he did when they asked him but not when the events happened. There were deep bruises on the girl's neck and his tongue was cut. He couldn't account for either condition. Fear and anger are terrible emotions and can put the mind in a state akin to shock: it rejects what it cannot bear. Roger didn't mean to kill Angela and he didn't know that he was squeezing her neck hard or biting his own tongue. She had caused him to lose the rabbit in the fire, his first meal in three days, and was threatening to report him for cooking it. Aside from not having eaten for three days, he had been starved for a year and undernourished most of his life. In his confession he didn't mention the broken neck until he was asked about it. Then he remembered shaking the girl to make her reasonable. He had no idea—"

Moulder started to object on the ground that no witness can say what is in another's mind, but he made a better point with the jury by checking himself and saying: "Oh, go ahead!" with a weary wave of the hand.

"He had no idea," Danby resumed, "that he was shaking her hard enough to break her neck.

"All of this happened on the level of the conscious mind, which was rejecting what the powerful emotions of fear and rage were forcing him to do. But we must go back farther still, into the unconscious mind.

"Roger's father died when he was eight, and from what he can remember of his father it was the best relationship in his life. One of his brightest memories is of a game his father used to play with him, pretending he would eat him until Roger would end the game by saying that he was too big and part of him would stick out. I believe that this innocent game had as much to do with his eating Angela's arm as the pressures upon him when he did it. Overlaid by ordinary and uninspiring human relationships after his father died, his harrowing rage and hunger brought it to the surface, and, because it had been a good experience, the little eating game innocently let down the bars of his inhibitions enough to let his hunger gain full possession of him. He was then only mechanically alive: his will and his sensibilities were asleep, and, as if he were an animal, he sought only to allay his hunger. His mind went away; it was in suspension; it was as if he had none; but as soon as his physical appetite was satisfied, or even partly satisfied, the ordinary guardians of his mind and spirit returned and again became paramount. He saw what he had done and in a compensating reaction threw up what he had eaten.

"At the time he pushed her into the furnace and then ate her," Danby concluded, "he was no more in command of himself than if he had been a Mongolian idiot."

"Cross-examine."

Moulder waited a moment in order to allow the jury to shift their attention to him and to prepare their expectation of the show that he had no intention of denying them. A new kind of quiet settled upon the courtroom.

"Doctor, how long would you say the defendant was a Mongolian idiot?"

"Objection," Morris said. "The doctor did not say he was a Mongolian idiot but that, like one, he was not in command of himself."

"I accept the amendment," Moulder said, bowing unctuously. "How long, Doctor?"

"I should say from about the time Angela started to scream until he threw up, say about twenty or twenty-five minutes at the most."

"He was sane before she started to scream and sane when he threw up?"

"Yes."

"And insane in between?"

"Yes."

"He is sane now?"

"Yes."

"How very convenient. Now tell me, Doctor—" Moulder went on, ignoring Morris's protest. But Morris would not be ignored and insisted upon his objection. Parkinsen, looking at him as if he had a foul smell, ordered the comment stricken. Moulder appeared to ignore Parkinsen.

"Doctor," he said, "how often did you examine the defendant?"

"About two dozen times and perhaps an hour at each visit."

"And the examinations, of course, were held in the prison?"

"Of course."

Moulder paused again and leaned forward in the fresh stillness.

"Do you ever have a patient lie to you, Doctor?"

Danby, taken aback by the unexpected question, also hesitated.

"Why—er, yes, of course," he said, "but not this one."

"Please answer the questions and no more. You took us back to the defendant's confession," Moulder went on. "I want to take you back to the autopsy of Angela Hake. You have read it?"

"Yes."

"And you have noticed the statement that male sperm was found in the uterus?"

"Yes."

"In his confession he makes no mention of a sexual attack on Angela, does he?"

"No."

"Does that have any significance, Doctor?"

"It does. It means to me that he did not attack her."

"Does it not also have the significance of being an untruth, or shall I say an evasion?"

"It does not."

Moulder grinned wanly. "It does not," he repeated and paused. "Now, you told us, did you not—and I shall try to quote you exactly—that 'the little eating game innocently let down the bars of his inhibitions enough to let his hunger gain full possession of him'?"

"I did."

"Then it is likely, is it not, that the same relaxing of

his inhibitions by the innocent little game could let his sexual hunger for her also gain full possession of him?"

Morris had no ground to object, for Danby had unfortunately said that he did not believe that Roger had raped the girl. This left him in a jungle of inferences, fair and unfair. If Moulder did not push his luck too hard and go completely out of bounds, Morris had only his closing speech to the jury with which to combat the prosecutor's tactics.

"It is not," Danby said decisively. "The sperm in her uterus, within the limit of a few hours, could have been anyone's."

"I suggest to you," Moulder persisted, "that he lured her into the schoolhouse basement as if to share with her the rabbit he was cooking, and raped her."

Morris objected. "That is unfair," he shouted. "A doctor cannot be asked to give theories of guilt or innocence, which is the province of the jury, but only expert reasons for sanity or insanity."

Parkinsen sustained him, but the jury had heard Moulder's suggestion.

"I move to strike the question from the record and ask Your Honor to direct the jury to disregard it," Morris went on.

"Strike it," said Parkinsen, gleaming. "The jury will

disregard it." The jury, however, did not seem to be doing so.

"You added, did you not, Doctor," Moulder resumed, "and again I quote, 'as if he were an animal he sought to allay his hunger'? If I said 'sexual hunger' it would also be possible, wouldn't it?"

"I am convinced he did not attack her sexually."

"I didn't ask you that. I said it would, if his inhibitions were relaxed, be possible?"

Danby had to admit that anything is possible.

Moulder paused, to take hold of a fresh subject.

"Now, Doctor, you used a phrase about the defendant's mind. You said that it 'went away.' Will you please tell the jury where a mind goes when it goes away?"

"I also said that his mind was suspended and that it was as if he had none. I was trying to describe his state of mind."

"Now which was it, Doctor?" Moulder spread his hands in mock helplessness. "Did it go away, and if so where was it? Was it in suspension, and if so what was it suspended from? Or was it that he had no mind at all?"

Danby sought help from the bench.

"Your Honor, he is twisting my testimony. Must I answer a question like that?"

Parkinsen eyed him grimly. "You must," he said.

Danby looked around as if to find an answer written somewhere.

"His mind was benumbed," he said. "It was where it always was, but it was clouded over."

"In a state of shock, perhaps?" Moulder inquired innocently.

"I would say so."

"Don't you know that if a person is in a state of shock he must be unconscious?"

"Medically, yes; psychiatrically, no."

"So you differ with the medical profession over what constitutes a simple thing like shock, do you?"

"I don't think we do, and we do not regard shock as simple."

"Who is 'we'?"

"Psychiatrists, or alienists, as we call ourselves."

"You might explain what you mean."

"We agree—of course—about the state of physical shock being accompanied by unconsciousness. But to this medical conception we add the psychiatrically stupefied mind, which is awake in its motor centers but is instinctually and emotionally unconscious. The super ego—"

"The *what?*"

"The super ego, or conscience, no longer functions."

Moulder sprang up and made a furious motion with

his hand. "In this case," he said, "you might call it the *supper eggo*. That's all."

One or two of the jurors guffawed. Morris got the crude remark stricken, but when he tried to straighten Danby out with a few quiet questions the jury barely paid attention.

Morris had to put Roger on the stand. The faint hope he had cherished, that Danby might get an even break from the jury, was gone. They had apparently approved Moulder's claptrap type of cross-examination and discounted the doctor entirely. The only hope was to put Roger on and let Moulder make mincemeat of him. If he minced him fine enough, the jury might turn back and feel sorry for him. Morris no longer thought that he had a chance of acquittal: it had been a faint chance at best. All that he could hope for now was life imprisonment, which the jury had the power to indicate by its verdict. It should not take much to make the difference valid. Two of the charges, the rape and the mutilation, were beyond reach, for with a jury the proof of each was too strong. The one real talking-point was that Roger had not meant to kill, and Morris put all of his pressure on that point. He knew that he was the hind legs of an emotional case whose front end could not be steered by logic, and if throwing his client to the dogs seemed cruel, it was the only chance left.

He waved the boy to the witness box. Roger gave him a quick glance, but he was prepared. Morris had led him through the various lines of strategy and had drilled him carefully in what he might expect. And he had held out no false hopes, for he needed his client's help and he would not get it if he chose either extreme of optimism or pessimism. He needed a witness who knew that he had to fight for his life and that if he did it well the chances were fair. He promised no more and no less.

He led the boy carefully through his story, making each favorable piece of it stand out cleanly and managing to give to each unfavorable piece some overtone that might at least invite discussion or hesitation. All that he could play for was that little cloud of doubt, more insubstantial than a reasonable doubt, which would swing the judging mind from death to life. So little, if only the judging minds were fair. He asked Roger to tell as much as he could remember of his early years, and Parkinsen let him, since he was on the defensive against committing error. The jury began to look at Roger, and Morris, cherishing every scrap gained, nursed his impossible case with high skill. Roger's fate at that point hung on a knife-edge. The story of the rabbit, the new job, and the threat of losing it made sense to depression people. It was a platform to rest on in the midst of the other horrible features of the crime. Morris held their attention to these normal reasons as long as he could.

But there was trouble ahead.

"Now, Roger, did you have sexual intercourse with Angela Hake on the evening of March 3 or at any other time?"

"I did not."

"Can you account in any way for the coroner's finding male sperm in her uterus?"

"I cannot. It had to be someone else's."

The good will that Morris had built up over the reasons for the killing might carry over to the charge of rape. The jury seemed to be hardening again, but it was difficult to tell. It all depended on the next few questions. He had gone over with Roger a dozen times how to put the stark truth in its most poignant light. The best that he could hope for was to make it sound like irresistible impulse, which was a human but not a legal defense.

"Did you, after Angela was dead, eat a part of her?"

"I must have, from the evidence, but I honestly don't remember."

"Did you know it was wrong to do so?"

"I cannot tell you, Mr. Longa. I was so hungry then

that nothing mattered but food. I didn't feel anything but food in my mouth. I didn't think of right and wrong. I had to eat."

"Did you kill her in order to eat her?"

Roger shuddered. "No."

The jury swung away from him and Morris knew that he had lost them irrevocably. He could see them stretch and look away. They had been hungry too but had never eaten anybody. He had nothing left with which to appeal and bring them back, save his closing speech.

"Cross-examine."

Moulder, able trial lawyer that he was, had also sensed the jury's reaction. The courtroom audience leaned forward eagerly. The great show was to begin, the destruction of the young cannibal's flimsy lies and excuses by pitiless cross-examination. But Moulder knew the difference between the audience, who had no responsibility, and the group of twelve who held the prisoner's fate in their hands because they were charged with the duty of deciding it. The jury wanted clear, sharp weapons and could be diverted from the proper use of them by the theatrics of slow torture. Quite sure of himself, Moulder shifted tactics. His voice was low and ice cold, and he never raised it or changed expression.

"The girl was with you in the basement?"

"Yes."

"There was male sperm found in her uterus?"

"It wasn't mine!"

"Your counsel asked Joe Hake if he beat you up once when all you did was to ask about his sister. Did he?"

"Objection," said Morris, rising. "Joe denied it and the District Attorney may not seek to impeach his own witness."

"This is cross-examination of the defendant himself," Moulder answered, also rising. "The interest of the People demands that I have the greatest latitude in showing just what he did. Besides, I have a different purpose from impeaching my witness." He glanced significantly at the jury.

Parkinsen paused over it. He was quite at sea, for it seemed like a new point to him. Although he wanted to favor Morris in his rulings, he doubted that he should do so when the District Attorney showed determination and gave battle. The portent of the question was lost on him, and he found himself pressed by two insistent lawyers. It would not do to antagonize the authorities, and he believed that Moulder would do nothing to get him into real trouble. He stroked his chin.

"The objection is overruled," he said, and all that Morris could do was to ask for an exception.

It was a questionable ruling and may have done Roger much harm.

"Answer," said Moulder.

Roger had to have the question repeated.

"He did," he said. With Roger innocently scoring against himself, Moulder could afford to pause before returning to his pointed questions. He made them sound like accusations.

"You choked her until her neck was crushed, didn't you?"

"I don't know! I didn't feel that!"

"You bit your own tongue halfway through while choking her, didn't you?"

"I didn't know! Later I felt it was sore."

"You shook her so hard you broke her neck, didn't you?"

"I don't remember doing that."

"You pushed her body partly into the furnace, didn't you?"

"Yes, I had to get rid of her body."

"When she was cooked you pulled her out and ate some of her, didn't you?"

"I had to eat. I was hungry. I didn't kill her to eat her! Some of her skin was on my fingers when I burned them and put them in my mouth."

"Then you realized what you'd done and you threw up?"

"I threw up, yes."

"And you ran away?"

"Yes."

Moulder got up slowly and looked at the boy with loathing.

"You remember all that and yet you say you were insane for twenty minutes while it happened?"

"I was. I couldn't say anything else."

"But you are sane now?"

"Yes."

"That is all." Moulder said it very quietly.

In rebuttal Moulder called Dr. McGruder. He was long and Scotch, and he was honest. He had an intellectual quarrel with the group in his profession that believed that insanity could be a short and even a momentary condition. He believed that insanity was the result, when it was not congenital, of a long process of deterioration, most likely cellular in nature, from which recovery was rare. What these young fellows were talking about was called irresistible impulse, and he didn't take much stock in that: too easy to simulate. Far from being irresistible, the impulse to commit a particular crime was one the criminal did not want to resist. For much the same reasons the Legislature had not made irresistible impulse a defense to criminal charges.

McGruder stated, testily and dogmatically, that Roger was as sane as he was: that no one can squeeze another's neck and shake another's head hard enough to crack a vertebra without knowing what he is doing; that if that were so, and it was, the person doing such things would certainly know that it was wrong to do them; and that anything to the contrary was a lot of rubbish.

Morris got the last remark stricken, even if Parkinsen did cast up his eyes as he ordered it, but the jury got vast comfort from the dour Scot. He had put into words what they all felt and what any person in his right mind should feel.

Morris did the best he could with him in cross-examination.

"When was it that you were called in on the case?"

"April 3," McGruder said, consulting his notes.

"That was a little over three months ago?" The doctor agreed that it was.

"In all that time did you ever examine the defendant?"

"I did not."

Moulder rose. "Counsel knows very well that the People's doctor did not examine his client," he said, "because counsel himself refused permission when I asked him."

He didn't want to make this speech, but he had to. Otherwise Dr. McGruder would have seemed inexcusably negligent in not examining Roger.

Morris rose in his turn.

"Mr. Moulder knows very well," he retorted, "that he had no right to have the defendant examined. I now ask Your Honor to instruct the jury that no one may be compelled to give evidence against himself and that I had every right to refuse Dr. McGruder permission to examine my client."

Parkinsen, looking as if he had swallowed something poisonous and was about to regurgitate it, delivered the instructions.

Morris had one more question.

"So your only chance to observe the defendant was when he was on the witness stand today?"

"That is right."

Morris sat down peacefully. The jury regarded him as if he were a magician who had pulled something unpleasant out of his hat. Court adjourned when McGruder left the stand.

Morris had only his closing speech left.

He could not sleep, but lay awake arranging his ideas.

He needed some phrase with wings to catch their imagination, if he could find it. When he saw the light come he got up and went to look out of the window, his gray hair rumpled and his slight figure boyish in his loose pajamas. He rested one cheek against the cool glass. From his house he could see the sea, and it began to catch in the rising fire of dawn. It was fresh and still: as if we ride the leading face of the world in the morning, where the air is clean, he thought. Seaward, the waves were in motion under the dawn breeze, slices of gun-metal in the early light with pearl blue between, and orange when the sun came up. He could imagine himself far out, a thousand miles from land, where Conrad said the peace of God begins.

Artema appeared with coffee. She knew the pattern well. He suffered during the dark, arose with the dawn, took coffee, lay in bed again with closed eyes and vacant mind, which rested and purged him of his suffering, and then lay with eyes open for two hours while he put his speech together with cold deliberation.

By eight thirty he was bathed and dressed and tranquil. He had breakfast and read the paper. Life was sweet and wide. He made love to Artema with his eyes and she returned it. They spoke little and of small things until he yawned and stretched before getting up to make for the door. She put her head on his shoulder a little extra long, and he could go without more, for they knew each other well. Both were fully happy that this was so, and all that she was would hold him through the day. They both knew what he was going to, but mere outcomes would not matter to them, because they lived by the quality of their performance and knew that this case was taking all that Morris had. That was good enough for Artema, and for him there would be only the far-off feeling, after, that he wished it might have been better.

Court opened briskly. Moulder apparently had lost little sleep, and Morris, watching him move about with his air of self-assurance, wondered at him. Moulder was running to paunch and had a moustache whose hairs flowed into sharp waxed ends. His head sloped backward like a steamer's smokestack, and vacant eyes looked out. He had not had great ambition. He did his job with native cleverness in a massive way that drew attention to him. Essentially bored with life, he found his outlet in work and did the weighty cases they gave him with a kind of capillary attention that went from point to point and left nothing out. Nor did it put much in. He got his results by bringing out all of the facts, and if there were difficult overtones which he did not quite grasp, he made ponderous fun of them as being outside of the average man's common sense. They made him

District Attorney and he supposed that someday they would make him judge. If they didn't he wouldn't really mind, but of course he wouldn't evade any chances like the present case. He had made his mark, and when he died they would put a bronze tablet to his memory in the courthouse corridor with massive words on it. Meanwhile he was on the side of authority, without wit enough to give offense, and rested easily on the line of least resistance.

Morris knew his adversary's habits and almost dozed through his first speech. Moulder merely outlined the charges and the evidence applicable to each. In even tones he demanded the penalty of death "for the most shocking, the most savage, and the most sinister murder in the history of our fair State." This did not take long, for he was saving his fire for his rebuttal to Morris's speech.

Morris rose. He felt relaxed and supple: it remained to find the lighted words.

"With submission to His Honor," he began. "Members of the jury:

"I have watched you during this trial, and it is obvious that you are against me and my client. But you are an American jury, devoted to the principles of fair play, and I ask you in the name of fair play to listen to me. I have only this one speech. Mr. Moulder can answer me,

but I cannot then answer him. I must therefore antici-
pate him.

"Roger Haike stands indicted of serious crimes, three
of them. He does not deny that he committed two, the
killing of Angela and the eating of part of her body. He
has denied the third, rape. Don't you think that if he
can admit the other two more serious crimes, and such
crimes, he would admit this also if he had done it? In all
fairness, don't you think that the sperm found within
her could have come from another man? There is no
proof that it was his except its presence in her and her
presence in his company. If rape were the only charge
against him, isn't it clear that you would have found him
not guilty because you should not guess whose sperm it
was?

"What are you to think of Angela? It is only in Court
that we speak ill of the dead, but we do it only when we
must, when another life depends on it. Surely you cannot think of her as the pure young virgin that Mr.
Moulder will undoubtedly paint her. How do pure
young virgins acquire an old and completely healed tear
of the hymen except by repeated acts of intercourse,
which the coroner's physician said she could have with
ease? With whom, at age thirteen, had she had such
widespread sexual experience? If Mr. Moulder tries to
convince you that it was Roger Haike, remember that

the State's own witness, Angela's own brother, told you on his oath that Roger hardly knew her. On whom was she trying to revenge herself, and why, when she entered the school basement with a man's semen in her body? I say to you that rape never occurred in that basement. There was no bruise whatever in the sexual area of that girl: the doctor said that too.

"Nor can the District Attorney take refuge in Angela's consenting to intercourse with Roger, which would be statutory rape because of her tender age. No, my opponent in his overzealousness to convict this boy has indicted him for rape, the old-fashioned forcible variety of sex unconsented to. Unless he proves that and nothing less, you must acquit my client of this charge.

"With rape out of the case, can you feel as strongly about the rest? If you have been saying to yourselves that a boy who rapes and kills and eats a girl must die, do you still say it if he killed and ate some of her, without the rape? There, I submit to you, is at least ground for the difference between death and life in your verdict. It shouldn't take much to make that difference for a boy still half a year short of eighteen.

"He is so young that the law will not let him vote or bind himself by contract: he is too young to drive a taxicab or get a detective license. But he is old enough to be killed. Yes indeed. Children as young as nine have been old enough to hang. In England, not here. I see it shocks you. Why does it? If this is a game in which a life must be given for a life, what difference is mere age? If one learns in Sunday school the difference between right and wrong, that knowledge becomes his death warrant and his age is immaterial. How barbaric can we get? I see you are still shocked by the idea of hanging a nine-year-old. Is Roger, eight years older, so much more mature and sophisticated that you are not shocked by the idea of putting him in the electric chair and roasting him to death?

"Do you really think that two wrongs make a right? Do you really believe that the sixth commandment of our Lord, 'Thou shalt not kill,' applies only to Roger Haike and not to you? That commandment does not read: 'Thou shalt not kill except by due process of law.' It does not read: 'Thou shalt not kill, but you may kill those who have killed others.' No. It has four words and no exceptions. Well, do you believe that commandment or don't you? If you do believe it, you cannot vote to electrocute Roger Haike. If you don't believe it, then look to your conscience in church next Sunday morning at eleven o'clock. And look sharp, for if you make a mistake there is no way, ever, to undo it. Then there would be two who cannot be brought back to life again, one at Roger's hands and one at yours."

The courtroom audience, like an animal heaving in its sleep, stirred and sighed. Morris glanced at them, but they only leaned forward as if to hear more clearly, and he went on:

"Let us look at the killing: the crushed and broken neck, his bitten tongue, his fear of losing his job. Are those the marks of a cold, willful, and premeditated murder? No. They are the typical signs of manslaughter —killing in hot blood upon sufficient provocation. Who in this jury box will say that fear of losing his job in these days is not a sufficient provocation? No one could so crush and break and bite unless he had been put beside his reason by the powerful emotion of fear.

"Even if you harden your hearts and think that his offense still stands at murder in the first degree, are not these telltale marks of fear and anger enough to spare his life? How much must you be moved to save the life of a seventeen-year-old boy?

"Most difficult is the eating of the arm. Mankind is singularly revolted by such a crime, and it is a very rare crime. It is so rare that we should look at it coolly and clearly, and if we do we discover that it is the low form of guilt known as a misdemeanor. No one contends, not even this bloodthirsty District Attorney, that Roger killed Angela in order to eat her. This is one of those wretched crimes that poison everyone's fair thinking and infect a whole case. I ask you to rise above that. Yes, of course, it is a dreadful thing to eat human flesh, but the eating of it had nothing to do with the killing or with the charge—the unfair charge—of rape. Nor does it carry the death penalty.

"You may recall from your school readers the story of how roast pig was discovered as a food. The house of a Chinese burned down and when he tried to recover the carcass of his pig from the ruins he burned his hands and put them in his mouth. That is what happened here: the girl's cooked flesh was on Roger's hand when he put it in his mouth. He had no thought of eating her before that. Had that been all, I am sure you would think little of it, but is what happened next so different in kind or only in degree? Will you give him no credit that as soon as sanity returned he was appalled by what he had done, that he vomited it up, that he ran headlong from it, and that he didn't try to hide?

"That brings me to the hard and final subject, the dark, mysterious cave of the winds that we call the mind. What I am about to say covers not only the mutilation but the killing too. They are separate legal charges, but his state of mind applies to both.

"Can you remember the last time you felt that you were going crazy? We use that phrase so much: he was driving me crazy; she is crazy; it was a crazy thing to do.

Why do you think that word crazy, which means insane, creeps so often into our daily speech? You must have felt so much pressure on you at some point in your life that if there had been just a little more it would have pushed you over the line. Or you were pushed over the line and had to stop what you were doing and perhaps go away briefly in order to break the connection with what was pressing in upon you. How long did it take you to recover your balance? Not long.

"You have had experience with other people's crazy moments. The man who blows his top, is obsessed with a single idea and is in a frenzy of anger when he is thwarted. Or the man whose sin is about to be discovered or whose precious thing is about to be swept away: what is the effect on him of his awful fear? In such anger or fear he may act crazily, even to the extent of taking his own life. You have had people yell at you in such anger that you say they are 'beside themselves.' Or cower in such fear that you say they 'are not themselves.' To use Mr. Moulder's type of question to Dr. Danby, who are they if they are not themselves, where and how far do they go when they are beside themselves? How soon do they recover? There are people who nurse their grudges for a long time, and there are people whose anger comes quickly and goes as quickly. In a matter of minutes.

"Are not these people, by our common speech, temporarily insane? There is nothing new under the sun. There is nothing strange in the idea that a cloud passing across the mind for a few moments can eclipse it as effectively as a solid and permanent overcast.

"Put in plain English, that is what Dr. Danby told us —that Roger was beside himself, was not himself while he committed these crimes, because of the enormous pressure upon him of fear and of days and months and years of hunger. The hunger of a growing boy is terrible indeed.

"Ladies and gentlemen, you cannot say that I am talking falsely! You know that I have accurately described rage and fear, and how quickly they can come and go. If you can admit that I am talking fairly to you, then how can you fairly send this boy to his death?

"Before you can do that and go on living with yourselves after today, you must be sure that you understand the processes of the human mind. I suppose you have seen insanity in its dreadful and pitiable forms— the imbecile who was born defective; the insane or psychotic who has, and he is Dr. McGruder's favorite, slid down the long ramp of mental illness into permanent disability; the moron who is below normal mentality but who can live safely if simply among us. By these standards no man is insane unless he gibbers and drools. My flesh-roasting friend here"—and Morris pushed an accusing forefinger under Moulder's nose—"wants you to believe that incoherence is the only valid symptom of insanity, that no one who can do things, however horrible, in a consecutive way or speak ostensibly sensible words can be mentally ill.

"By those standards no one can have tuberculosis unless he spits blood, or gangrene until his arm or leg falls off, or pneumonia until his lungs are full of ichor. They require actual eating away of tissue, visible rotting, tangible invasions of flesh or bone. What a limited view!

"Do *you* know what the life force is? Well, do you? What is it that passes through the nerves and causes pain? Am I talking nonsense? All right, what is electricity? Can you see it or touch it? You know very well that you cannot. You can see only what it does, its effects. Isn't it fair to say the same of the nerves and of the mind? You cannot see how it stores away the things it remembers. You cannot see whether its means of transmitting thoughts, colors, ideas, reactions, and recollections are free and open or tragically jangled and short-circuited. What are the mechanics of sanity and insanity? If one is sane, is the reaction to the color blue, for example, stored in one part of the brain, and if one is insane is it stored in another part? You don't know, and I dare say the doctors don't either.

"We are all of us, doctors and laymen, like Hansel and Gretel, wandering lost in a wood whose paths we cannot see. How dare you, then, send to his death a seventeen-year-old boy whose mental processes you do not understand! If two doctors of ability and distinction do not agree about them, how can you? On what basis will you say that one has the right of it and the other the wrong? Are you going to decide this case on the basis of paying your nickel and taking your choice?

"I trust not. A human life is at stake. I ask you to believe Dr. Danby and to disbelieve Dr. McGruder because Danby knows better than McGruder the effects of the subtle brain whose causes, straight or twisted, neither of them understands any better than you understand electricity. Look at Danby's testimony. He talked about all the known factors in Roger Haike's life, about human emotions whose effects anyone can see and does see every day, and about the results of these emotions on the mind, judged by what actually happens. Once upon a time people died of what the doctors called 'inflammation of the stomach': now the cause is known to be an appendix which can be removed, and people live. Dr. McGruder demands evidence of cellular destruction in the brain before he will admit insanity: he is like the doctors of a hundred years ago who talked about inflammation of the stomach. Dr. Danby knows we cannot see the brain's electricity in its passage over crossed wires, but he can see the effects, even if no cellular changes are visible: he is like the modern doctor who removes the appendix.

"How *do* you get from the physical to the moral world? How are 'good' and 'bad' registered in the brain, or 'right' or 'wrong'? How is red or blue? How is an elephant or a microbe? You can't tell, but you are asked to pass through a brain whose essential processes you cannot understand a huge charge of force called electricity whose method you don't understand either, and thus to kill that brain. My God, what arrogance! Who asks it? A saint or a god with some mystic authority? Oh no: it's Moulder, the District Attorney, who asks it, nay, demands it. Moulder, with his little waxed moustache and his coarse puns about a supper eggo."

Again the spectators seemed to move in unison, and Morris felt that they were favorable to him. Juries were on guard not to show their reactions during a speech, but the crowd felt no such restraint and he could test on them the impact of his words. He braced himself to close: the need for the lighted phrase was now.

"Are you so sure you know the difference between right and wrong? I hasten to say yes, you do. But be sure you remember where your knowledge comes from. It doesn't come from God: if it did, you would have to obey His commandment and not kill Roger Haike. It comes from a criminal code written by State legislators in a book. What they wrote there is average behavior: it isn't refined or subtle, like the mind, it is the big broad path of human conduct that applies to most people. The law can't do any better unless it gets help. It can get help from you. If you give an answer to this case that is wise and merciful, you will help to make the law wise and merciful. If you send Roger to his death, you help to keep the law where it is, killing people who don't agree with it and who rebel against it because they can't do better without the help we give them. You cannot say, can you, that within the next fifty years, which is Roger's life expectancy, nothing can be done to make him a valuable citizen? If you deny him that chance, then our system of law, forged in the fires of tyranny and oppression, is no better than its molders (the pun is apt but not intentional), and we are all damned to a system of vindictiveness and revenge. We should only punish to restore and by restoring forgive.

"I say to you again, in closing, that you must be very sure that you yourselves know the difference between right and wrong before you vote for this boy's death. You will be told in the deadly Mr. Moulder's most persuasive tones, and again by His Honor, that the State has the legal right to kill. Despite what you are told, be

sure that you feel you have the right to send this boy to
his Maker before his Maker calls him in His own good
time. You do not have to answer to Mr. Moulder or to
His Honor, but you must answer to your own conscience, to your Maker, who is also Roger's. What are
your credentials to do this grievous thing? Any other
penalty set out by man you may freely give when there
is cause, but I say to you that the giving and the taking
of life is God's right alone. The distinguished flesh-
burner who opposes me may tell you that the same Bible that reports the commandment not to kill also reports the right to take an eye for an eye and a tooth for
a tooth. But he will look far before he finds in the life
of Jesus the authority to take a life for a life.

"But there is a little more, this side of Heaven. We
are made in the image of our Maker: Holy Writ says
that too. If so, His mercy and His love are the guides of
our feet and the counselors of our hearts, upon appeal
from our minds. Even if you do not believe in God,
there is for the agnostic the tender loneliness of the human family, the unearthly and terrible march from dark
to dark. We know that other people look out from eyes
like ours upon the tragedy of the world and feel with
hearts like ours the common misfortunes of mankind.

"I have argued to you the question of Roger's acquittal because of the momentary disaster to his mind. I

have argued to you his right, if you believe him guilty, to the law's mercy known as manslaughter. Beyond these I shall not argue but will presume to demand the right to take Roger Haike's life with me through the courtroom door, even if our paths divide there and he goes to prison for the great sum of his remaining days. I say to you that a little of his life will go with each of you, but that if you take his from him he will take a part of yours and that it will live in the prison whose mercy you denied him.

"I leave his destiny in your hands, and may the unspoken prayers of all the Rogers in the world and of suffering humanity as well go with you."

He sat down quietly. The courtroom was hushed, for he had moved them, jury and audience and Court professionals. Artema, sitting in the back of the room, hid her face in her hands.

Moulder got up slowly. He knew the power of a good speech and knew also that it did not necessarily mean anything in the final outcome. It might or it might not. The real effect of Morris's speech was to add a question mark which was easily within the prosecutor's power to erase. To get up quickly and shatter the silence with a loud or sudden statement would be dangerous. There was no harm in giving to Morris's effort its full value.

Moulder did this, knowing just what to do to wipe the effect of his opponent's words from the jury's minds. He did not even address the Court, but began straightaway: "Members of the jury:

"There is a saying in the law that when a lawyer has a weak case the thing to do is to damn the other lawyer. Mr. Longa has done a good job of damning me, calling me bloodthirsty and deadly and a flesh-burner. He has seen fit to refer to my moustache and, after scolding me for a pun, has then made one himself that links my name with tyranny and oppression. He has called me his opponent, knowing that we are here to do justice, both of us, from our different positions: hence he makes it seem to you that I seek injustice.

"If it is injustice to rid our city of a cannibal; if it is injustice to destroy one who destroys our innocent children by pushing their bodies into furnaces; if it is injustice to bring to book a raper of young girls—then I do indeed seek injustice. But it should be called Justice, in fair capitals, that goddess in whose hands are the sword and scales of equal treatment and whose eyes are blind to prejudice and privilege. She will give to this young beast the same Justice he gave to thirteen-year-old Angela, but with this difference: her death was unmerited, his is fully merited.

"This lawyer here"—and it was Moulder's turn to

shake an accusing finger under Morris's nose—"has seen fit to brand this dead girl, this thirteen-year-old child, as a precocious and experienced strumpet. For shame! He has quoted her brother's testimony that they hardly knew each other. And how does her brother know that? Because he didn't see them together? Isn't it the first rule of seduction that the seducer and his victim shall not be seen together?

"*There* sits Angela Hake's seducer! *There* is the man who first put the marks of womanhood in her body! Let us blame him but not her if in the innocence of her youth she let him have his way with her for weeks or months, we know not.

"But her brother knows more than appears on the surface. You will recall my asking this Roger if Joe Hake beat him when all he had done was to ask after his sister. Joe had denied it. I said then that it was not my purpose to impeach Joe by contradicting him out of this young monster's own mouth, and the wise judge who presides at this trial perceived my purpose and allowed my question. How modest of Angela's brother not to want to play the hero who had defended his sister's honor by knocking her defiler down! He preferred to deny the incident instead of capitalizing on it. But he knew what had been going on! How effective to wring from the defendant's own lips, however unsuspecting of my purpose, an admission that his victim's brother had done what any red-blooded young American would do in defense of his womenkind!

"Lawyer Longa asks for proof of violent rape. He shall have it. His client had seen to it that no new marks of sexual attack could appear in the usual places. But I say to you that we are fortunate in having evidence of the strangulation bruises to the girl's neck: I will spare you the horror of a description of her head, on which you may infer from its position in the furnace that no evidence of any bruises could survive. If you ask why a man must force a woman who hitherto has been compliant, I admit freely that the reason is locked in death: but there can be no stranger answer than the one that Mr. Longa gives, of the girl bursting into the schoolhouse basement with another man's semen in her body. What a desperate explanation, without rhyme or reason! But there is reason, in Joe's conduct, to point the finger at defendant Roger Haike."

Moulder paused to take a drink of water and glare at the defense table. Roger had gone white and was asking Morris to stop the flow of the District Attorney's incredible argument, but Morris could only shake his head ruefully and whisper that Moulder could say anything that was relevant, whether it was true or false. It was Roger's first experience with the difficult truth that if a thing is legal it cannot stink.

Moulder faced the jury and resumed in a lower tone.

"Which among you could walk our streets in peace and confidence, knowing that this young fiend still lives? Who could sleep quietly in his bed at night? Which parents among you could believe that your daughters would be safe? He seeks complete release because he was insane at the time of his dastardly acts but has recovered his sanity now. He feels entitled to no punishment whatever! He asks you to escort him to the courtroom door and there to set him free! To do what? To rape and kill and burn and eat again? Perhaps it would be a tender child of five next time—the flesh of such a child is soft and sweet indeed. I see you wince, but my duty is terrible and I will not shrink from calling a spade a spade. Freedom without restraint or hindrance is what he wants, freedom to rape and kill and eat.

"Suppose you should find him guilty of manslaughter. In not more than ten years, and maybe less, he would be out again, older and wiser in cunning ways to assuage his abnormal appetites and spurred on by hatred of those who imprisoned him, perhaps you yourselves.

"Suppose you find him guilty of murder and send him to prison for life. He might escape. He might be pardoned: the average length of commuted life sentences in this State is fifteen years. If you yield to softness and false sentiment—and God forbid that you should!—I urge you to add to your verdict a direction that he shall not be released before the end of his natural life.

"How silly and futile are these lesser penalties! There is only one deserving penalty, one manly and womanly thing to do to protect our homes, our children, and our fair name, and that is death. Do not shrink from imposing it, for you will be giving to him what he has already given to that innocent girl.

"My learned friend has seen fit to quote Scripture, which a great poet has said even the Devil can do. We who stand in the place of law and order and common decency can quote it too, that we should do unto others as we would have them do unto us. Roger Haike has shown what he would do unto us by what he has done to one of us: so, in the name of the Holy Writ that he invokes, let us do the same to him. Our method is clean and orderly: yea, it is merciful, a quick death by that very electricity that Mr. Longa spoke so eloquently about. It is better than slow and cruel torture by strangulation, by breaking of the neck; cleaner than pushing a body partly into the fire; more decent than the revolting eating of Angela's sweet young flesh.

"We do not seek a life for a life. We seek the equality

of Justice, which here happens to involve a life. The equality we seek is based on the common sense of the average man, the man who walks our streets, does our work, sits in our jury boxes. This is no demand for a life, but for the cleaning of the slate so that men and women may walk fearlessly and our children play in safety.

"We seek no victims. We ask no vengeance. We are here to protect the society of which we are a part, and to clean our house.

"Again I say, give us all our due—a verdict of guilty and a penalty of death."

A long sigh stole through the courtroom as he sat down. Artema was seated next to a buxom young matron. "That's straight talk, that is," the woman said in a low tone. "The other fella, well, in other words, I mean, he made a good speech and all, but all it was, he made you feel sad, like when you have to shoot a horse that's broke its leg. He wants out, and my God, he *ate* her! Know what I mean?" She did not wait for a reply. Parkinsen was fumbling with his notes, getting ready to charge.

Parkinsen, for all his venom, was shrewd, and he could tell how things were going. He had had to fight hard to get to where he was in life, and no one could tell him anything about insanity. The law was an old and venerable institution, and if it was good enough for the great English judges and for the judicial builders of our American law, it was good enough for him. Anybody who had fought his way to eminence in the law, as he had, knew the difference between right and wrong. A man knew about that as soon as he was old enough to know about anything, specially if he'd been raised in politics, as he had been. He didn't know much law, but he knew enough, and he knew a lot about the type of man that could get him appointed to the State Supreme Court. All he had to do was to attend to his knitting and preside over a few important trials that would go the way of law and order. This was one.

That fellow Longa, now: funny name, that—must have come from the Soviet Union. Parkinsen pronounced the first syllable to rhyme with sob. Ought to go back there and take his screwy ideas with him. (Morris was a generations-old American, out of Italy originally.) Well, they wouldn't get far in this case, not if he could help it.

He had his definitions of the crimes written out, and he read them. He also had written down the elements of first-degree murder as set forth in the old leading case of *State v. Fife*, 1 St. Rep. 58, and he read that. The doctrine of reasonable doubt and the legal test of insanity followed, with approving emphasis accompanied by sharp glances at the jury from under shaggy brows. He then outlined the facts and showed how the law might apply to them. He briefed the testimony of the witnesses, using a flat and colorless voice for Dr. Danby and Roger and considerable animation for Dr. McGruder. He concluded:

"If you believe that defendant, circumstanced as he was at the time, knew the nature and quality of his act, or if he did not know it, knew that it was wrong to rape and kill and eat the deceased, then a verdict of guilty would be proper, with the penalty to be fixed by you on the murder indictment at life imprisonment or death in the electric chair. Of course, if you believe that he did not know the nature and quality of his act, or, if he did know it, that he was unable to distinguish right from wrong at the time of these offenses through not knowing that it was wrong to rape and kill and eat the deceased, you should acquit him on the ground of insanity, and in that case he will be continued in custody until it appears that he can safely be released. Or you might find him guilty of manslaughter or acquit him if you have a reasonable doubt of his guilt, in accordance with our earlier instructions."

Impeccable language, but eye and mouth and gesture put obvious accents on the key words. Morris felt sick.

Roger leaned over to him. "How does it look?" he asked.

"Never can tell about a jury," was the best that Morris could manage.

"I know," said Roger slowly. "They are going to burn me."

Parkinsen recessed Court and the jury was led out to deliberate. The spectators gathered in groups outside of the courthouse and discussed the case.

Morris's office was across the street from the courthouse, and he went there and lay down on his sofa. He was tired now, and he dozed off into a world of turgid images. His secretary wakened him. "They've agreed," she said. "They've been out an hour and five minutes."

Morris groaned. " 'The shorter the time, the longer the rope,' " he quoted. He got up and returned to Court.

Parkinsen came out and the jury was led into the box.

"All rise," the clerk said. "Jurors, have you all agreed upon a verdict?"

"We have," the foreman answered.

"Jurors, look upon the prisoner. Prisoner, look upon the jurors.

"Mr. Foreman, on this bill of indictment charging Roger Haike with rape, what is your verdict?"

"Not guilty." Roger gave a little start of pleasure and looked up happily at Morris, but the lawyer's face was grave and his hand tightened a little on the boy's arm.

Parkinsen had raised his head and was glaring at the

foreman of the jury. He stared composedly back at the judge.

"Not guilty by reason of insanity?" Parkinsen asked him.

"No, Your Honor, just plain not guilty."

The judge's displeasure was apparent and he seemed to be about to say something, but he finally lowered his head over his docket book. He had already written "Guilty" in it and was now having to make room for the unexpected extra word.

Later investigation revealed that number-twelve juror had once read law. He had reached the jury room after the charge in a state of high excitement. "We can't convict this Roger of rape!" he began shouting almost as soon as they had seated themselves around the worn round table. "It could have been another man as easy as him." "Why was the girl in the basement at all, then?" one of the other jurors asked him. "What difference does it make what she was in there for?" the young juror replied. "Maybe he did rape her. Maybe she went there to eat some of his rabbit. Thing is, I'm afraid the judge isn't so hot on his law: made a couple of bum rulings, and I think he should have told us to throw out this rape charge. It's one man or another, and it's an equal guess. That's bad. So is what the coroner's doctor said. There's no evidence of sexual force. The Supreme Court could grant a new trial and maybe the next time something would happen and let this little so-and-so get away with it. We've got him dead to rights for killing her and eating her, and there aren't any mistakes in the case about that, so why take a chance of upsetting the apple cart over this rape? Let's agree among ourselves that he's as guilty as hell of it. But it's doubtful legally, so let's throw it out and burn him for sure on the other things."

The three women wanted to find Roger guilty and argued that the Supreme Court would treat the charges separately and make the State try only the rape over again. The legal juror said it couldn't happen that way and that a new trial would involve all of the charges. After some discussion the other jurors agreed to the verdict announced by the foreman.

"Proceed," Parkinsen barked at the clerk and again looked angrily at the foreman.

"On this bill of indictment charging Roger Haike with the mutilation of a dead body, what is your verdict?"

"Guilty."

"On this bill of indictment charging Roger Haike with murder and manslaughter, what is your verdict?"

"Guilty of murder in the first degree. The penalty is death in the electric chair."

Roger shot a quick look for help at Morris. It did not seem real until the foreman said the terrible words. Reality now came close, the game that seemed make-believe was suddenly grim, his loneliness at once terrifying. The grown-ups had won after all, unless the little man with the rumpled gray hair and the lined face could work magic. But it was touch and go, and the magic must come quickly.

His look went unanswered, for Morris knew that there was no hope and his face was empty. He made the usual motion for a new trial, and Roger clutched at it. Surely there would be a new trial. He would have to go through it all again, but he guessed it was the only way. Argument was set for a month hence. He was led away to his cell.

Above their heads Parkinsen was booming to the jury. "The Court gives you its thanks for a courageous and proper verdict," he said. "Never within the Court's memory has there been murder more foul and disgusting, but we are fortunate in having as a bulwark against the jungle the institution of the American jury. You are now free to return to your homes with the gratitude of the community."

I wonder what was so courageous about it, Morris thought to himself: it was what everybody in town wanted, from the press to the members of the Ladies' Civic Association.

.   .   .

Roger's mood swung between wild hope and deep despair, for the words of the extreme penalty allowed for little but extreme emotions. He looked endlessly out of the barred window at his small slice of summer, now heavy and stagnant at mid-season. The idea came to him that his moods were as changeable as the weather, and all that he could summon from the thin resources of his past was the memory of the long straight beach, the flat sea, and the wet sand that was like sealskin. It was the only bit of grandeur he had known, and it brought him the companionable loneliness that Nature can offer to a needy soul. It was only now and then that he felt thus comforted, for he was young, and depth of spirit was a new dimension to which he was unused.

He grew even slighter and seemed to be all eyes. When Morris entered the cell he would see the boy turn from the window and fasten his large eyes on him. At such moments he wanted to retire from the law, for Roger's gaze was a raw, suspended plea for help or for news that the rough game was over and he might go. He still could not accept the verdict as final or even as applicable to him. Morris found the visits very trying, as there was little to say, but to appear regularly seemed to him a kindness, the predictable presence of the one friendly person on whom Roger could count.

Morris filed a petition for a three-judge Court to pass

upon his motion for a new trial. It was customary to grant such a petition in capital cases, and Parkinsen had no reason to refuse. He picked as his colleagues Judges Studdard and Polk. Studdard was a new, young judge, weak enough to feel honored by the invitation to sit with older men. He would look solemn and, nodding slowly, would give it as his considered judgment that a new trial be denied. Polk, all teeth and brisk, had no eyes for anything but the record: if no errors appeared, he would vote to uphold the verdict, whatever it was. Parkinsen chose well.

The three judges sat and glared at Morris like angry oxen. Polk asked what errors Morris was complaining of and when he heard none that appealed to him, lost interest. Studdard sat silent, trying to look wise and patriarchal. Morris argued the community's prejudice and the unfairness of not changing the venue. He then concentrated on Roger's lack of intent specifically to kill Angela.

He argued subtly and well and had Studdard thoroughly bewildered. But the young man's only point of wisdom was to keep silent and follow the lead of his elders. Polk, stretching his mouth to show his teeth and drumming his fingers on the conference table, declared that he saw no reversible error.

Parkinsen let a week go by, so as to seem to have

given the case deep thought, and then overruled the motion for a new trial. He filed a short and truculent opinion and summoned Roger before him for sentence.

This was his supreme moment, his chance to play Moses to the community. He was its totem Justice and he would stand there in the flesh and give judgment as if he had just stepped out of a thick cloud onto a mountaintop. He memorized the sentence, but wrote it in large letters on a card to put on the bench where he could read it without appearing to, if he forgot. He practiced before a mirror—expression, gesture, and flashing eye. The whole case would suddenly be focused in him. He would pronounce Justice and for a moment actually be it. Done just right, it might produce his nomination to the State Supreme Court when the next vacancy occurred. For a fleeting moment he even felt gratitude to Roger.

Roger, benumbed, stood at the bar beside Morris. Parkinsen advanced to the bench with measured tread, cast a piercing glance around the courtroom, paused for a dramatic hush, and threw back his head.

"Does the prisoner wish to say anything before sentence is pronounced?"

Roger stood dumbly.

"The sentence of the law is," Parkinsen resumed, speaking to the ages, "that you be taken hence by the

Sheriff of the County to the place whence you have come and thence in due course to the place of execution. There, during the week to be appointed by the Governor of the State, a current of electricity of strength sufficient to cause death shall be passed through your body and continued until you are dead. And may God have mercy on your soul."

This time Roger did not look to Morris for help. Morris had told him what the next steps would be. He heard the dreadful words of his punishment, and it was as if everyone in the courtroom receded into a milky whiteness in which he remained, stark and alone. Even life receded, leaving the little naked unmoving kernel that was himself, spiritless and bodiless, to surmount as best it could the awful idea of death. He looked for a moment at his hands, seeing the fingers move in their accustomed way and feeling their movement against each other and his palms. These were to become dead and useless by some process he could not imagine. He wondered where death would enter and clutch him.

Again he was led away to his cell.

Comment

A COURT TRIAL is the hub of the legal wheel, the process for which the law provides the ground rules. It is the arena for private warfare, the area of combat for the ultimate settlement of legal disputes. Yet it is the weakest part of the system. It is no better than the men who use it.

All democratic civilizations require public demonstration of error, from the tribe sitting in a circle to Cicero denouncing Catiline or Lord Coke prosecuting the Earl of Essex for treason or Clarence Darrow pleading for the lives of Loeb and Leopold.

Serious as a trial is, it still has the theater's air of illusion. The past must be reconstructed and a present sanction applied which will extend into the future. It is rather awesome thus to cover the whole continuum of time.

Most business people run their affairs by the law, of course, but not by Court procedures. They settle and rarely litigate, but their decisions and settlements are made in the light of what might happen to them in Court if they got there.

What would they see if they did get there? It is quite possible that they would see a fine inquiry into the rights and obligations of man, especially in a civil case involving the settled rules of property. This is mankind at its best, eschewing the field of battle and settling its disputes around the table. But they might also see the tragically jangled wires of a trial like that in *State v. Roger Haike*, a trial conducted ostensibly according to the rules but doomed, as Roger was, to the foregone conclusion of death by the prejudice and cruelty of the community's fixed ideas.

There is another kind of case, where sweetness and light suffuse the trial but where the horror has already happened. Here is such a case.

A man aged twenty-three was arrested and charged with the fatal shooting of a policeman. He came from ne'er-do-well parents and had a minimal education, most of it in an orphanage after his parents died. His only relative, a sister, was living with a gangster who used him as an accomplice for snatching pocketbooks. The boy finally broke away from this evil influence and moved to another city, where he married, had a child, and got a job. While visiting his sister, who was very ill, he was picked up and charged with the murder of the policeman. He was held incommunicado for four days and questioned for another week. He was denied counsel and food and was not only questioned for long hours by relays of detectives but was mercilessly beaten. The police refused to tell his wife where he was. At length, broken in body and mind, he confessed to the crime on the assurance of the detectives that for his co-operation he would receive a light sentence. Completing his co-operation, he pleaded guilty and was stunned to hear the Court pronounce on him the sentence of life imprisonment. After he was taken to the penitentiary he was visited by detectives and, not much caring what he did, signed another confession which covered some rather glaring gaps in the original.

Do not believe that the third degree is nonexistent. This story is extreme, but its like can happen when evil men get control of a large metropolitan police force.

It may be even harder to believe that there are many people who do not know that civil liberties exist, who feel that all of the power of organized society is against them, from the arresting officer to the judge, and who are convinced that the best deal they can make is to confess to anything.

It took this man nine years before he had so educated himself and restored his balance that he felt that he could make a move to free himself. He then filed a petition for a writ of *habeas corpus* and it happened to catch the eye of a sensitive member of the State Supreme Court. That body ordered a lower Court judge to hold a hearing and ascertain the facts. The hearing lasted a week, and the Court found that the defendant had a good alibi, that the confessions had been coerced and were untrue, that almost every tenet of due process had been violated, that there was no competent evidence against the defendant, and that a new trial should be granted. The new trial was a formality. The District Attorney joined with defense counsel in asking that the defendant be acquitted. This was done. He had served twelve years for an offense of which he was wholly innocent.

If this case seems to be an odd freak, four similar ones could be cited that have happened within the past five years in three of our largest and oldest States: New York, Illinois, and Pennsylvania. In the New York case the innocent prisoner, who had served twenty years, was given $112,000 by the Legislature and died two months after receiving it.

Or they might see the case of *State v. Johnson,* a man who killed and fled successfully. This is not too difficult, since we catch no more than one in five of our felons. This one went to a distant State under a different name, settled down, married, raised a family, and became a respected member of the community. But eventually he was recognized and reported by a lynx-eyed patriot. Twenty years after his crime he was returned to the State where it had happened and put to his trial. Those who were watching the Court heard the trial judge say this to him:

"You have pleaded guilty to this old crime, Johnson, and if you had been tried twenty years ago it is certain that you would have gone to prison. It may sound unjudicial, but I am sorry that you were recognized. The inquisitive citizen who turned you in could have spent his time to better advantage.

"From your blameless record in your new life I can imagine that you have served your own sentence in your own prison. No one who kills, unless he be a professional killer, is apt to forget the experience or to forgive himself save in bitterness and humility of spirit.

"You may find your new home a bit less friendly than before, but from the many letters your counsel has shown me, I should say that the people who matter will be your even more loyal friends. You may go back there now, for there is little purpose in a prison sentence unless it be to make a man again a useful citizen, and you have managed that unaided.

"Wishing you well, I now suspend sentence."

A courtroom runs the gamut and almost anything may be seen there. Much has been said about the law's being scientific, and some sort of case can be made for that, short of Court. Once in the arena, however, the rules of law change character. No longer are they conduits conducting thought, but trading-posts around which human destinies are wrought in passionate fires. It is here that the real result is had, the social sanction applied, reputation and perhaps career shattered or vindicated. It is here that the massive safeguards given the accused leave him, upon conviction, and shift to society. It is here that presumptions harden into fact or dissipate and the score is added up and tallied for all to see. No matter what may happen in the Appellate Courts, the public verdict in the trial Court is final: men know when a win or a loss has been had by a clean fall or on points or by disqualification, and judgment goes accordingly.

Let there be no talk of Efficiency. It is easy to dream up ideal systems, and we could have efficient trials if we

took six weeks over every case that now takes six hours
to try and if we could tolerate the country knee-deep in
judges and social workers. And if we had Mr. Hitler's
crisp ideas of sterilization and breeding and euthanasia,
and his notion that the inefficient ones are those that dis-
agree with us. No: let us be sparing of efficiency, especially in those human institutions that depend upon
words for their proper focusing. Efficiency must be tidy,
and a penitentiary is tidy to the point of madness. Let us
remember what Aldous Huxley says in his introduction
to Piranesi's terrible and unearthly etchings of prisons:
"The good life can be lived only in a society in which
tidiness is preached and practiced, but not fanatically,
and where efficiency is always haloed, as it were, by a
tolerated margin of mess."

The criminal law is the black sheep of the legal family. It is anything but lucrative for the average practi-
tioner. To the leaders of the bar it seems not quite nice,
for gentlemen never get themselves arrested and hence
it is convenient to treat the criminal law as if it did not
exist. Like sin, if one is against it in others, one has done
away with it in oneself. Chief Justice Taft called it
medieval as long ago as 1912, and the only major new
idea that has grown in the field since then is that of pro-
bation and parole.

Actually, the criminal law has remained medieval with minimum damage to the populace. There is little law in it. There are the definitions of the crimes, a few aphorisms about trial procedure and evidence and sentencing, and the great monuments of civil liberty, like the right to trial by jury, to confrontation by one's accusers, to the benefit of a reasonable doubt, and to due process. Murder, robbery, assault, rape, and fraud have been quite well understood since the days of Julius Caesar.

If the criminal law is so simple and static, whence comes the difficulty that we feel in weighing the extreme results achieved in *State v. Roger Haike* and *State v. Johnson?*

There are two answers: the growth of the Welfare State and the growth of psychiatry.

In the early 1930's the ideas of unrestricted competition and of the economic survival of the fittest seemed to have come to the end of their tether. The fittest often succumbed, open competition created bread line and soup kitchen, and God rather than the devil was apt to take the hindmost. Something new had to be done quickly, and it was done, from securing the stock market against pirates to creating old-age pensions. The public began to feel that there were no more forgotten people, and folks with these ideas in their heads began to fill the jury boxes. They also stood at the bar, charged with crime. If the Government was refusing to fling people aside, the Courts should not fling them aside either. Juries began to condemn fewer people to death. Defendants in the large cities began to entrust their trials to their superiors, the judges, rather than to their peers, the jury. The army of The People became an army of single men and women whose individual rights had become perceptible.

At the same time the great wind that Freud had set blowing in man's mind was blowing in the same direction. It blew upon them all in the medical and allied sciences—the physician, the sociologist, the psychologist, and the psychiatrist. All of these began pounding for admittance on the courthouse door, for what could be more individual than the working of a mind? Wherever we looked the single man stood out, and the more we understood of him the more single he appeared to be. And what appeared with increasing clarity was that he must indeed be presumed to be a little mad.

It is also growing clear that the importance and effect of free will are becoming less and less as a person's early influences and motivations are revealed. Psychiatry can show their grip upon him to explain his past action and, by helping him to understand his plight, free him from similar pitfalls in the future. As man develops in moral caliber, his choice of the right action will become increasingly automatic. And as psychiatry develops its techniques, it will increasingly help him to keep clear the path to instinctive choice.

All of this has raised difficult problems, above which the law bends a troubled ear, and the most difficult is the responsibility of a criminal for his crime.

Lawyers and doctors are at cross-purposes. The law presumes men sane, psychiatry presumes them mad. Both are furious because it seems impossible to draw the line between harmless and harmful madness. The psychiatrists know that the line can be drawn, but they know not where. The lawyers know where to draw it, but they know not how. They talk on different levels. There are too few psychiatrists, and they do not always agree with one another. Many a hung jury has resulted from the jurors' feeling that if doctors cannot agree, how should laymen be expected to? This suggests the single Court-appointed psychiatrist, but if that be done, the adversary form of trial is invaded.

Lawyers, with public business to do, must have a test of legal responsibility as a device for deciding guilt or innocence. They argue that the test for determining a fact must be the form of mental effort that we call knowledge, and that mind and body must assume mutual responsibility for their actions. The doctors say that a man may know right from wrong and yet be incapable of doing right; that they cannot testify in terms of moral judgment or assign a certain amount of psychopathology to a given amount of legal responsibility; and that the only valid terms are those of compromise behavior which seeks relief from inner tension.

To complicate the difficulty, the average man in the jury box has his own standards, different from those of both the doctors and the lawyers. He finds it necessary to blame people for their actions. If you were the victim of a rape or a robbery, the temptation to blame your attacker would be well-nigh irresistible. In fact, you would probably want to kill him barehanded.

The public's attitude is that it cares less for the prisoner who inflicted pain on others than it does for the pain to be inflicted on him in return. This is vengeance. It is also deeply inconsistent, for, as every practicing judge knows, it is only other people's friends and relations that should go to jail. The public enjoys its drink of blood. It also has its own crisp ideas of what is right and wrong and is going to take no nonsense from a skull doctor who talks a strange jargon about the id, the super ego, and the subconscious mind. Knowing this, the lawyers are inclined to let loose their powers of sarcasm. The cross-examination of an earnest psychiatrist can be cruel—witness poor Danby.

All three actors in this Mad Tea-Party are scurrying conscientiously about and are managing to improve things a little. Juries are sentencing only about seventy people to death each year, compared with double that number before the last war. The lawyers are increasingly using pre-trial and pre-sentence investigations and psychiatric explorations of one kind or another. The psychiatrists are trying to simplify their processes in order that reliable opinions may be distilled from shorter treatments and examinations. But this is not enough.

There is no way around the confusion except to keep the psychiatrist out of the courtroom altogether and to let the Courts continue to find facts. The trial is not the proper port of entry for psychiatry into the legal system. The only place and the most effective place for it is in penology, following conviction.

We need a new term. Let the Courts go on "finding deeds," or what happened in the case at bar. The psychiatrist will become the one who "finds facts," the facts of personality and behavior, and on the basis of these facts proper treatment will be tailor-made to fit the patient.

What stands between psychiatry and the law is the M'Naghten Rule, still hale and hearty after a hundred and sixteen years. In 1843 M'Naghten tried to kill Eng-

Comment

land's Prime Minister, Sir Robert Peel, and to the day of
his death thought that he had, but he had actually killed
Sir Robert's clerk. He was tried and acquitted on the
ground of insanity, whereupon such a hue and cry
arose—part of it from Queen Victoria, whose life and
whose husband's life had also been attempted during
her reign—that the Law Lords were asked to formulate
the law of insanity. Their answers, though advisory only,
have become embedded in our law. The important part
of them reads as follows:

> *To establish a defense on the ground of insanity,
> it must be clearly proved that, at the time of com-
> mitting the act, the party accused was laboring un-
> der such a defect of reason, from disease of the
> mind, as not to know the nature and quality of the
> act he was doing, or if he did know it, that he did
> not know he was doing what was wrong.*

This is still the law in England and in thirty-one of
our States. In fifteen other States irresistible impulse is
allowed as a defense. This means that a man may be
acquitted if he knows the difference between right and
wrong but is irresistibly impelled to do what he knows
is wrong. One State has no clear test. In New Hamp-
shire, now followed by the District of Columbia in the
recent case of *Durham v. U.S.*, the rule is: "A person is

not responsible for criminal conduct if such conduct was the product of mental disease or defect."

The American Law Institute is now working on a general Restatement of the Criminal Law. It has suggested for continuing study the following formula as a substitute for M'Naghten:

> *A person is not responsible for criminal conduct if at the time of such conduct, as a result of mental disease or defect, his capacity to appreciate the criminality of his conduct or, if he did appreciate it, to conform his conduct to the requirements of law was so substantially impaired that he cannot justly be held responsible.*

To change the law in forty-six States is a formidable task. Difficulties of clarity and principle over the word "know" in the M'Naghten Rule are matched by difficulties over the words "product," "disease," and "defect" in the Durham Rule. M'Naghten is one of those doctrines, like the law against obscenity, that are so dear to people's prejudices that the effort to change or repeal them raises a clamor out of all proportion to their worth. But the Rule's field of operation has been greatly narrowed. Remember that it applies only to a defense made in Court during a trial. It has nothing to do with psychiatric approaches before or after trial. These are now so directed by modern Mental Health Acts that no man incapable of making a defense can be tried, and his incapacity is determined under the Act, not under the M'Naghten Rule. The Rule, therefore, now applies only to the case of a man who asserts that he was insane when he committed the crime but has since recovered his sanity and demands not only acquittal but his freedom as well, an assertion that would strain the credulity of any reliable fact-finder or reputable psychiatrist. Hence the Rule is rarely invoked, but whether it will die on the vine depends on other things.

Though M'Naghten is rarely used, his mere existence makes him potent. He is more than a Rule: he is a philosophy. If it is wrong to rob, it is right to punish the robber. This dichotomous right and wrong is not true cause and effect, but it seems to be, and hence it keeps our legal process punitive, the keystone of a vengeful penal system.

It may be that when we think of insanity we are too prone to think that only psychiatry can determine it. There are cases where a defendant's insanity could appear without an alienist being called to testify. The law of England was different before the M'Naghten case. In 1723 Justice Tracy, using Coke's and Hale's definitions, said that in order to avail himself of the defense of insanity a man must be totally deprived of his understanding and memory, so as not to know what he was doing any more than a wild beast. This rule was changed by *Hadfield's Case*, in 1800, when the law on the subject stood at its highest point before or since.

Hadfield, a brave soldier and loyal to the King, had been so grievously wounded in the head as to be unbalanced. He believed himself to be the savior of mankind, and was convinced that he had to become a sacrifice, as Jesus had done. To achieve such martyrdom he had to be executed, and he thought that the way to be was to attempt the King's life. This he did, but was forestalled and put to his trial for high treason. Thomas (later Lord) Erskine defended him on the ground that a man could know right from wrong, could understand the nature of his act, could use cunning and foresight in executing it, and yet be so mentally deranged that he should not be held accountable. Lord Chief Justice Kenyon put the case to the jury on that theory and they acquitted because of insanity. Hadfield was continued in custody.

By 1812 contrary decisions were appearing, and England has not returned to the enlightened rule of *Hadfield's Case*, nor have we adopted it in America.

It would be a mistake to supplant M'Naghten suddenly. Neither law nor psychiatry is ready for such a change. There are not enough psychiatrists, and there are no appropriate legal standards waiting to fit their doctrine. Best to keep narrowing M'Naghten's place and squeeze him to death by putting the full legal-psychiatric emphasis upon the processes of punishment—or treatment, as the penology of the future will call it. As these processes improve there will be less and less need for M'Naghten, less and less need for *mens rea*, the guilty mind, as a necessary factor in crime, and less and less need for the adversary method of trial, which will ultimately be supplanted by some form of impartial inquiry. The only need for psychiatry at trial will be to determine *mens sana*, whether the prisoner is too insane to plan his defense, and the measure of sanity will not be the M'Naghten Rule but the psychiatric rule.

We must consider, in the nearer future, the effect of the new conception of penology on the adversary form of trial.

Trial by combat of wit is now reckoned the law's most potent method of establishing truth. The thrust and parry of cross-examination and the clash of story against story is indeed apt to reveal the more likely explanation of a disputed event for the judging mind, whether Court or jury, to select. It is also true that after a good fight a man can with better grace accept a verdict that may not be wholly accurate. The mere energy of combat generates, like a duel, a kind of self-approving afflatus which makes acquiescence in a compromise more tolerable. This is one reason why cases are settled during trial.

The purpose of a trial is to impose or evade civil damages or criminal sanctions. A man will fight like a tiger to avoid going to prison, while he would not fight as savagely against going to school or going to hospital. The same energy he now exerts in trial he would exert, under a new system, in improving himself and shortening his period of detention. Any restriction of liberty will arouse some opposition, but if the restriction is beneficial his initial opposition should be no greater than making sure that the need for treatment is fairly and clearly shown.

The fact that the adversary trial is the best the law has achieved thus far is no reason for thinking that nothing better is possible. The adversary trial and M'Naghten should both die on the vine as penology discards vengeance and adopts effective methods of rehabilitation.

Let the Courts go on finding deeds. There is much to do to cleanse and sharpen this process. Put the doctors, the sociologists, the psychologists, and the psychiatrists in the prisons to determine by all available scientific means how long a man should stay there.

This is no great step. It was not more than four hundred years ago, in England, that no distinction was made between sane and insane criminals. An imbecile who was guilty of criminal conduct was imprisoned and chained to the wall along with the convict of sound mind. We have come a distance by requiring the presence of *mens rea* in crime. It is no greater distance to stop requiring it and replace it with something better.

This sounds like work for legal and medical scientists exclusively, but that is not quite so. Left to themselves, juries show considerable independence. If a judge is too severe, the jury may acquit where ordinarily it would convict. With the unpopular Volstead Act in the days of Prohibition, juries turned everyone loose, regardless of the evidence, and went home to their illegal highballs before dinner. When moved by sentiment, juries conclude that a defendant should not be required to suffer the consequences of what he undoubtedly did, and they acquit him.

If Roger Haike's jury had been interviewed after verdict, they would probably have said that the little beast was of course insane to do such things but that their very frightfulness required his death. Psychiatry has yet to win the full confidence of the public. The cussed truth about M'Naghten is that, for all his pedantry, he bases pretty squarely upon mankind's average common sense as this has been developed in the habit of assigning blame, and hence we stand in some danger of throwing the baby out with the bathwater.

But if law and psychiatry find it hopelessly difficult to achieve mutually satisfactory trial procedures, the two professions can easily unite in preparing the public mind for psychiatric penology. The public will fall in line quickly enough when they see their friends and relations emerging from prison mentally and socially improved.

There are some startling ideas to get used to under the psychiatric conception of guilt and punishment. One is that the protection of society as a single objective is better than the porridge of punishment, correction, rehabilitation, and social protection which we now serve up in the same dish. A corollary to this is the notion that the average murderer is so appalled by what he has done that he is less a social menace than the confirmed pickpocket and should probably spend less time in confinement. That the determination of guilt, of human motivation and responsibility, and of treatment form one indivisible process which should not be broken into parts is good psychiatric doctrine. It often happens that a man is so purged by remorse for his crime that he is no longer an actual menace to society and need not be brought to trial at all. There are some who commit crime because of a submerged hunger for punishment and atonement and who should be made aware of it by treatment rather than given punishment which may not exhaust their hunger for it: hence even a determination of their guilt or innocence may be unwise. There are some, possibly like Willie Sutton, who seem incapable of using freedom but who become model prisoners and may even have a valuable message for mankind so long as they are kept locked up. That motive and responsibility are profoundly difficult things to evaluate and do not fall easily into the obvious categories of right and wrong is good doctrine. And there are some men, of whom more anon, who are incurable, unreformable, and even unpunishable. They are the mad dogs, and they do not always snarl and foam.

One major line of trial development is the form of sentence. The wholly indeterminate sentence is suspect because a man who has lost his liberty wants to know or to be able to figure when he will get out. The new form of sentence should include a short and flexible minimum, a long maximum, and an intermediate period, fixed by a diagnostic or parole board, of psychiatric, medical, and sociological procedures of an increasingly educative nature.

We must have regard for semantics. Punishment is a

portmanteau word, like justice: both may be good, bad, or indifferent. I am careful not to say let us abolish punishment, for the word has the root sense of penitence, but let us abolish a criminal system of laws and sanctions based on vengeance. Let us treat and educate, and let the inmates call the process what they will: all that matters is the quality of the product.

We must be careful not to underestimate the violence of the public's feelings of vengeance and desire to fix blame. What we are trying to do is to change the rules of war, and that is not done lightly. We think highly of due process because we want to keep inviolate our right to take an eye for an eye: revenge protected by rules of fair play amounts to holy war. The public has historically shown great jealousy of its control over the Courts. In our system of government there are not three but four great checks and balances. Besides the executive, the legislative, and the judicial there is the inertia or the violence of the public, which holds the brakes on the other three and is equally important.

To sum this up, the assumptions are that the trial is part of a punitive and not of a curative system, and that its future is to cease to be an adversary proceeding and become an impartial inquiry; that the M'Naghten Rule is the keystone of a punitive penal system, psychologically but not actually, because it occupies only very narrow ground; and that the proper place of psychiatry in the law is not in Court but in the prisons.

We cannot solve these problems if we think in terms of mass. It is in terms of one man and then the next that we must think: one man, with his food, his family, his work, his faith, and his value to us. If we are to think of man and not of men, then we must achieve considerable humility and lower the sights of our personal ambition in order to see around us more clearly. We need big men who are willing to become trial judges. We need even bigger men who are content to remain in practice and represent the broken and desperate people who face indictment and trial.

As one grows older it becomes apparent that a man's size is not measured by his title. "I will not make an over-large gate to my little city," said Arthur Warwick in 1637, and Plutarch might have added what he said so many centuries earlier: "As for myself, I live in a little town, and I choose to live there lest it become still less." An anonymous Englishman has summed it all up: "I have beaten the parish bounds and found them to contain the whole creation. I have stood by a stall in the market-place and trafficked with the Indies. I have gossiped with John Stiles in the street, and heard in his voice the voices of all of the children of men."

III

The Execution

IN A FEW DAYS Roger was transferred to the death house.

This was located in a prison near the center of the State in an isolated spot. It was the most massive and secure of the State prisons, and it would have been impregnable in an age when walls were all that was needed to keep people out. That age being long past, the walls were now used to keep people in, and all that beat upon their outer face was the despair of distant relatives and friends. It may be that the encircling fosse and ramparts were intended to prevent attempts at rescue, but none had ever been made, since sorrow is gentle and unarmed.

Set on a slight eminence of land, this fortress seemed to gnash its teeth and glare grimly at mankind, for here was the electric chair and its apparatus of death. The unnecessary fortitude of the place would have been funny, except for the chair's infallibility. Here too were kept the State's most dangerous and hardened criminals.

The only entrance was by a steep defile in the hills through which ran a road and a single spur of railroad track, used for bringing in supplies and prisoners. In this defile were two solid gates a hundred yards apart which formed a lock, and within it all automobiles and railway cars were thoroughly searched. This area was the end of the line for the railway. The second gate was then opened for automobiles and pedestrians. The ground between the gates was bare and flat. Searchlights were trained on it from towers set upon the overtopping walls. Guards carrying rifles or submachine guns patrolled between the spaced towers on walks along the top of the walls, the inner sides of which were studded with broken glass and iron spikes set into the masonry.

The inner gate of the lock was the entrance to the prison itself and was double. In the space between these inner gates automobiles and pedestrians were again inspected before passing into the prison compound. Walls and buildings were of dirty brown stone, and the outer wall of the prison buildings was a secondary security wall barren of windows and higher than the inner part of the structures. This wall was generally circular, and within it the various prison buildings seemed stuck onto it. The prison was not the panopticon type, for experience had shown that if the guards could always have the prisoners in view, the reverse was also true and the inmates always knew exactly where the guards were and what they were doing. The administration, utility, and shop buildings were built against the wall, and the cells were in one long three-storey building standing separately in the center. The ground between buildings was cemented, and although the prison was set in rolling woodlands and farming country, no green thing grew within the walls except in pots in the Warden's office.

A section of the cell building farthest from the gate was two storeys in height and was set off from the rest of the structure by a solid stone partition. The only entrance was from the compound directly into this section. Here were the death cells and the chair, on the upper level. Below were machinery and the reserve generators, always started at times of execution in case the public utility should fail.

The second storey was reached by a special iron stair one man wide. At the top were a small landing and a double steel door, requiring a separate key on each side. Once through, a short walk led to another solid steel door also requiring two keys. This door opened into a small forecourt to the cells about twenty feet wide. To the right, a barred gate let in to the six death cells. To the left, a special black door revealed the chair, its electrical apparatus, and the seats for the official witnesses. The condemned prisoners were, in short, securely locked in.

The cell area was divided between cells and open corridor. The six cells, a bath, and a room for the officers ran side by side along one outer wall, cell Number 1 being nearest to the forecourt. Those awaiting execution were stacked so that the latest comer was put in the cell farthest from the door and worked his way along as the nearer cells were emptied. The chair always claimed its next victim from the cell nearest it.

Each cell was ten feet long by six feet wide and seven high. The construction was of stone. The cells contained a hopper, a sink, a bed, a table, a chair, and a Bible. Nothing else was allowed unless it was other religious books, but if these were put together with wire staples, the staples were removed. There was no window. There were two windows in the wall opposite, separated from the cells by the fifteen feet of open corridor where a guard was always on duty. If a man stood on the edge of his bed, a view might be had through the window downward into the compound. Otherwise the only things visible were the inner prison wall and a bit of sky.

There was no light in the cells, but a bright light in the ceiling of the corridor shone through the barred gate of each cell and was on night and day. Inmates could talk to each other from cell to cell, but could not visit.

Each prisoner, upon entering the death cells, was given a white shirt, a pair of white socks, a pair of black trousers, a pair of black slippers, and underclothes, all of very poor quality. This clothing had no pockets and no metal.

There was no toilet paper. It had to be requested. If a man had been in his cell long enough to be allowed cigarettes, while his appeals were in process, he had to ask the officer on duty for a light. There was a small wire cage in one corner of the corridor screened with heavy mesh, for visits. The wire was so thick that it was difficult to recognize from without who was in the cage. Letters addressed to an inmate were read to him through the bars by the officer on duty.

Exercise was allowed, not more than three men at a time, in a special part of the prison compound fenced in with barbed wire. Nine armed guards lined a walk thirty yards long while the inmates, chained together, walked for forty minutes each fair day. They were not allowed to talk or to pick up anything that might drop.

A doctor visited the death cells daily, to be sure that everyone was in good health for his approaching end.

No medicines were allowed unless a man was ill and the prison doctor prescribed. As the prisoner in the cell next to Roger said to him shortly after his admission: "It takes an Act of Legislature to get an aspirin tablet."

Each prisoner's head was shaved bald upon admission, and his face was shaved once a week by an officer. He was also allowed one bath per week. The head-shaving was repeated every six weeks if a man remained that long. The reason for keeping the head bald was to prevent the hair from catching fire during electrocution and allowing the head to become a torch.

Roger was taken from the County prison to the death cells by railroad. The transfer was usually not made until after a prisoner's appeal had been disposed of by the State Supreme Court, but except in the very largest cities, where maximum security was assured in the County prisons, the local authorities were eager to be rid of a man under sentence of death: he might become desperate. In Roger's case, the dreadful nature of his crime, added to the death sentence, made him a doubly fearsome character in the eyes of all who beheld him or who had the responsibility for his custody. The death house was not full, and there seemed so little chance of such a clear case being reversed that with Judge Parkinsen's permission, readily given in the form of a Court order,

Roger was hustled out of town and put into death cell Number 3.

He stayed there, working his way down to Number 1, for three months.

As a murdering cannibal he had proved rather disappointing. Perhaps he was expected to foam at the mouth and roar. No one had been allowed to see him, between sentence and transfer, excepting the press, who descended upon him in full array. Photographers, haunching tensely and lensing aptly, popped and snapped at him. None of their pictures was published, for by this time Roger was a scrawny little fellow with no foam or roar in him. Reporters plied him with questions about how he felt about his sentence, and what he thought it would be like to die, and what he had felt while he was eating Angela. To all of these Roger turned terrified and uncomprehending eyes, which were translated to an avid public as glaring defiance.

By mischance, a batch of Roger's mail, which he had refused to read, fell into the hands of an alert reporter. The letters came from all parts of the country. There were letters proposing marriage in the death house: one of the young women explained frankly that it would cost him only a few minutes of time, while she, effectively insulated by prison regulations against the possibility of conceiving his child, would gain considerable fame and perhaps a Hollywood contract. There were letters asking for money, on the theory, also frankly stated, that he wouldn't long be needing anything that belonged to him. One writer threatened him with personal vengeance if he should finally escape the supreme penalty, which was too good for him, especially since the writer said he had proof that Roger was a nigger. Others offered to take his place in the chair. One suggested an elaborate plan of rescue for a substantial fee, the only difficulty being that the escape was described with reference to the jail in the writer's own small town in a distant State.

This correspondence aroused the town newspaper to a steaming editorial. Its point was to invite all such letter-writers to stay at home and mind their own business. Had an obvious sentence been added, it would have shown the paper's clear policy to be that the town should be allowed to burn its own malefactors with undisturbed self-complacency. The paper had once published an editorial to the effect that punishment should be tailor-made to fit the criminal, and except for the sequel this was very fine. The sequel was that since no such tailoring system existed, every murderer's head should be chewed right off his shoulders, that other criminals should be made to serve time until it ran out of their ears, and that judges and members of parole boards who suggested leniency should be impeached or removed from office.

The newspaper had a most gratifying increase in sales during Roger's case. It would do anything for money, even, now and then, a good deed.

At first it was a relief to Roger to get away from the scene of his crime and trial. Since his sentencing he had felt like a swimmer in surf who miscalculates and is banged against the bottom, rolled over and over, filled with sand and water, and swept up barely alive on the foreshore.

Believed to be a desperate character, he was shackled to a burly detective and put aboard the prison train. There was only one carriage consigned to the up-State prison, and it had half a dozen seats specially designed for prisoners. The rest of the space was for supplies and baggage. Here he was also secured to a ringbolt below the inch-thick unbreakable glass window, and this arrangement required him to sit where he could see out.

It was a five-hour ride, all but the last hour of it in daylight. Away from the littoral, the way first led through flat rich farmland and then began to climb. The landscape hardened a little: there were outbursts of rock and sudden thick forest on sloping uplands.

Roger felt spent. For months he had wrestled with

the strange problems of his case as the needs of the trial had shaped them. He had had to become articulate, which was against his nature, and he had said more words than he knew existed. They had done him no good, for here he was on his way to his death and he had no real faith in the Supreme Court or the Pardon Board or the Governor. They were the steps that still lay ahead, but they were unreal. If the people on the spot damned him, he had little to expect from people remote from him. He rejected them on this last ride, all but Morris, on whom his mind rested wistfully and with love. Morris, who had fought so hard and had only been appointed by the Court to defend him. He was the one person who stood out in Roger's mind with shape and form. All the rest were blurred—the tough hard ones, the knowing ones, the righteous ones. They all sank into oblivion, and only Morris stood out more clearly than before. He wanted Morris. He wanted to keep hold of him to the end, as if he were thread and continuity, the only thing that could abide and make a final, rounded experience, short and twisted as it was. He needed continuity: otherwise he would be lost and broken. He had asked Morris to come and be with him, and Morris had said that he would.

He went slack and fell back in his seat. The thick glass showed green, but he could see out if he looked directly through it. The trees and pastureland slipped by, with now and then a house and a man sitting behind his pipe. He has seen the prison train before, Roger thought, and he is wondering who is in it. The idea of an impersonal human being steadied him, and it occurred to him that there was none left in his life. Suddenly he felt that life was over indeed, that he had had his allotment, and all that remained was to break down his body and create a death. Nothing he could ever do would change the fact that he was the man who had killed and eaten the little girl. He felt sorry that he had done it, but he couldn't see how he could have got out of the trap he had been in. It was wrong to kill and eat her, but those were words in a vacuum. One of the newspaper reporters had written that Roger showed no signs of remorse. He puckered his brow, wondering how remorse is shown. He would show some if it would help and if he could decide how it should be done. He thought that Angela might have shown remorse before she started scream-ing. After that he didn't see how he could have altered anything: whatever happened had followed inexorably from what had happened just before. He was bewil-dered, but he felt no rancor, even toward Angela. What was remorse? If they let him live, he might find some. He couldn't yet figure how his body, so responsive and supple, could be wrenched from life. There must be dreadful and unbearable pain. Once in death, what would it be like? If life had been so difficult and so tricky, how could he have courage to face another and unknown state? He felt through with life, though not with living, and he couldn't quite understand that. He wondered if he would brush his teeth, go to the bathroom, change his shirt, and sleep, when he was dead. All the small familiar motions of living held him to life, which, in great and comforting principle, he was through with.

The long shadows came and lay east. Then they left with the sun and it was dusk. The train was crossing a ridge, and there was a long view over a valley and a river to a low range of hills beyond. It grew darker and Roger strained his eyes to see the last of his world. Then darkness fell and there was only the rough and grimy interior of the prison carriage. Existence narrowed abruptly, and fear came again. There was nowhere to look now except at the dismal things around his feet. He felt lost—more lost in life, he hoped, than he would in death. A great loneliness fell upon him.

The train stopped and in a few minutes crawled forward. They had entered the first gate and stopped again while it closed behind them. The burly detective unlocked Roger from the ringbolt, and at a signal from the trainman they got out.

There was a walk of seventy-five yards or so to the next gate. Roger could sense the shadow of great walls climbing the ravine, and of the massive gates. The searchlights almost blinded him as they began to walk. Still handcuffed to the detective, followed by two guards with tommy-guns in their hands, watched by others similarly armed on the walls, the slight figure of Roger Haike scuffed his way across the dusty ground to the second gate. It swung open and he entered a cavern of steel and stone. As it closed behind him the other gate moved to let him through. Prison guards now took him, past the cell block to the small section at the far end, in a locked door, up the winding iron stairs, through the double door and then the steel door into the forecourt. Hardly pausing, he was ushered through the barred gate into the death-cell corridor, and as the guards held their guns on the occupants of cells Numbers 1 and 2 the steel bar that locked all cells at once was released, the barred door to cell Number 3 was pulled open, Roger was pushed inside, and the bar replaced.

He would be processed in the morning. Meanwhile he was very secure and could not get out.

He was given his issue of clothing, and his head was shaved. He felt shy about his bald head when he went out for exercise, for the windows looking down upon the exercise yard had eyes in them, the eyes of inmates watching the condemned. They seemed a permanent part of the windows, for they were always there, set in heads that moved slightly now and then but looked without ceasing.

Roger grew more than ever silent. It was comforting to be quiet and not racked by words and questions. He had little to say to his two fellow prisoners or to the guard on duty, and the same continence in language kept him from reading. The Bible was the only object in his cell besides the bed and chair and table, and its unfamiliar words failed to interest him. He looked for stories of fights and battles in the Old Testament, but they didn't amount to much, and Christian doctrine bewildered him. He walked up and down, his mind empty, passing the time. Only the thought of death started his brain working, but now that he was here, next door to the electric chair, the idea was even more remote than it had been before he came. This mood did not last.

A week after his arrival, cell Number 1 was emptied of its occupant, whose name was Harry Bellz. He was taken out at the usual hour of execution, half an hour after midnight, and the day preceding it was not pleasant. He had been high-strung and nervous before and was given to alternating fits of mania and depression, but with a cell between them Roger had not been greatly disturbed. During his last day Bellz whimpered and cried most of the time, but now and then he roused himself to seize the bars of his door and shake them savagely, crying out to know if his pardon had not yet come. When he was told at about six o'clock in the evening that the Governor had refused to intervene, he gave a great scream and fell to moaning. Once he began banging about in his cell, and two guards had to go in hurriedly and prevent him from injuring himself badly enough to prevent his execution.

This had occurred when the generators on the floor below were tested by the executioner. The lights suddenly dimmed and a low hum was audible, while the whole cell-room vibrated gently.

Roger could not see him, since the cells were side by side, but he sounded like nothing human. He was like an animal bounding about in its cage and uttering strangled cries of fear.

He started screaming when the Deputy Warden and the guards rolled a screen from the far end of the cell corridor to the end of Number 1 cell, to hide from his view the witnesses who were filing into the death chamber. Replacing the screen, the guards unlocked the cell bar, holding guns on Roger and his neighbor, and tried to take Bellz out. The prison chaplain stood by and then led the way, but Bellz never saw him.

It took four guards to carry him from his cell, bladder and bowels open, shrieking and struggling. He cursed and prayed and pleaded for mercy and promised to lead a good life. They surely couldn't mean to take his life: how else could he live and get along? He had things to do, things that urgently needed finishing, important things he hadn't told anyone about yet. He kicked and fought and flung his rigid body about, his eyes rolled back and his face distorted by animal terror. Foam flecked his lips, and his nose began to bleed. Hoarse from screeching, he croaked obscenities as the struggling guards forced him through the special black door and slammed it behind them.

From beyond the black door the muffled yells and groans were still audible, until there was one final and terrible shriek. Then silence at once and the sound of a small clap of thunder, followed by an extra buzz. Roger, frozen with horror, heard Pengo, his neighbor, say calmly: "First jolt." In about two minutes there was a sound like two steel plates crashing together, the switching off of the current. Twice more the cycle was repeated. Then silence. "Hmph," said Pengo contemptuously, "only three. Thought he'd take six at least, after all that exercise." He started to whistle.

A special guard returned and cleaned up cell Number 1. Then, with two others holding guns on them,

Roger was moved into cell Number 2 and Pengo into Number 1.

"Pengo at bat, Haike on deck," his neighbor remarked to no one in particular. Ordinarily he was as silent as Roger and only once had yelled at Bellz to shut up, which Bellz instantly did. Pengo had authority and his voice had an edge. Bellz didn't stay shut up, but Pengo lost interest and did not try again.

When silence fell Roger fainted. The guard opened his cell, threw some water in his face, and left again.

"They all do that the first time," he said, locking the bar.

"The hell they do," Pengo said coldly. "I didn't."

"I was talking about people, not you," the guard remarked. "You're ice. When they turn the juice on you, you'll shatter."

A week later it was Pengo's turn. When the Warden came to say that if he wanted anything special, within reason, he could have it with his last dinner, Pengo laughed harshly. "Cigarettes. I don't feel like eatin'," he said shortly.

He smoked incessantly, but said nothing else the entire day until they finally came for him. The chaplain came first, and when they opened the cell he held out a cross. Pengo pushed it away and stepped out one pace, as he had been directed. A guard with a pair of scissors came forward, and, bending down, slit Pengo's trouser legs from the knee to the bottom. The guard then undid the two top buttons of the prisoner's shirt, to make it easy, later, for the doctor to apply his stethoscope. While he stood there the chaplain again offered the crucifix.

Pengo gave the chaplain a cold glance and grimaced. He was smoking a cigarette. He threw it on the floor and pointed to it. "Stamp on it," he said. "Hellfire's your job." He turned away and as the guards came to assist him he brushed them aside and walked leisurely but steadily through the black door. Roger tried to count. From the time Pengo left his cell until the first jolt he made it fifty-three seconds.

There were only two jolts.

The guard on duty looked after him, shaking his head. "Coldest sonafobitch was ever in here," he said. "Know what he done? Killed his wife and kid because they bothered him. Said she snored and the kid cried. Said his wife was a slut and his kid was a bastard. Just got up one night and slit their throats. Crazy guy. Better off dead."

Number 1 cell was swabbed out and Roger was moved into it.

*   *   *

It was during his last visit to Roger in the County prison before the boy was transferred to the death house that Morris promised to come to see him there. The combination of shyness and urgency was irresistible. Roger did not say it very well, but he managed to let Morris know that he felt alone and faced, in youth and health, the inexplicable process of being abruptly destroyed. Had he known it, he was as much afraid of dying first, from sheer terror. It might have been easier to die by his own hand, had he had the means of doing so, but death seemed more terrible because of all the human beings who would focus upon him the awful power of their attention, their vengeance, and their diabolical machinery.

He wished that he might march bravely to a wall, as he had once seen in a motion picture, and there be blindfolded and, after making a moving plea for the salvation of mankind, be heroically shot. That would be a proud way to die, vital to the end. Creeping in slippers to the stark arms of a wired chair in the middle of the night would take away what little self-respect he had left and put horror in its place.

He and Morris had sat silent for a little while, with nothing left to say, and Morris had arisen to take his leave. Roger was fidgeting.

"What is it?" Morris asked.

The boy gave him one appealing look and dropped his eyes.

"Will you come when they do it to me?" he asked. And Morris, almost before thinking, said that he would. He would come and tell him the Supreme Court's decision, if it was unfavorable, and he would also come on the last day.

Morris had never witnessed an execution and had no stomach to, but he felt that he could do no less when Roger asked him. The boy had no one else to turn to in his extremity. Morris tried to imagine his loneliness, if no one came, and shuddered. He would go, and Artema said that of course he should, and when, almost as shyly as Roger, he asked if she would come with him and wait for him in the small town near by, she gave a little cry and threw her arms around him and said that she would go with him.

Morris worked hard over his brief and argument for the Supreme Court. He now argued for the first time that since Roger had been acquitted of a felony, one of the three charges against him, the penalty on the other two should not, as a matter of law, have risen higher than life imprisonment. It was a novel point, and the Supreme Court had the power to reduce the sentence accordingly if it agreed with him. He also argued that Parkinsen's questionable ruling, even though Roger had been acquitted of rape, allowed Moulder to argue as he did to the jury about Joe's knocking down his sister's defiler and about his being such a modest witness: all of this tainted the case to Roger's detriment.

His argument would have at least one result. It would force the Supreme Court to write an opinion and not dispose of it summarily, and someday research would have the case to point to, with all of its facts and law appearing in the opinion. Roger's side of the case would appear in Morris's brief, which, with the testimony, was preserved in bound volumes for posterity. It was the last thing he could do, to leave "an ember yet unquenched" for the finger of history to pause over.

The case was heard on the preferred list, as all capital cases were, on the first day of the autumn term. The Judges had read the briefs beforehand, and they had read the newspapers too. They had decided not to question Morris, who therefore had to work up his own breeze in argument. He did so very well, using up all of his allotted time, and Moulder had to answer him more fully than he may have wished. Speeches of counsel were reported at trial but not on appeal, and Morris had Artema sit in Court and take down his and the prosecutor's arguments. Moulder, not knowing that he was being recorded, praised Parkinsen's discretion in the case but took leave of his own and was so intemperate that for a moment Morris hoped that his opponent had overplayed his hand. In any event, the argument, preserved in his file, would make interesting reading for the historian.

He did not have to wait long for the decision. The Court filed its opinion about two weeks later, affirming the judgment in the peculiarly remote and bloodless language that the legal profession can achieve when wanting to express its decision to keep its hands off something. Morris's arguments were brushed aside as having no merit or as being no more potent, legally, than an unsuccessful appeal to the jury. The juror who had read law smiled to himself when he saw this: "The contention that the trial should have been held in a distant County because of local prejudice is refuted by the jury's action in acquitting the defendant of one of the charges. We see no reason to interfere with its other conclusions or with the penalty it saw fit to impose."

It sounded as if someone had taken the case into the desert and left it there.

The Governor, shortly after, fixed the first week in December for Roger's execution. This allowed time for application to the Pardon Board and for its decision.

Morris journeyed to the prison to tell Roger the Court's decision and to have him sign the necessary papers for application to the Pardon Board for commutation of his sentence to life imprisonment. Conversation through the thick mesh of the visiting-cage was difficult, and this was doubtless so intended, but talk was unnatural to Roger. He needed other forms of approach and touch, and it was enough that the older man had come and asked to see him and had spoken to him and spent a few minutes there.

"I'll be back," Morris said, "if things get worse, but let's hope they won't. There's no law left in the case now, and often that's good."

He felt Roger's large eyes on him.

"It won't be any use," the boy said. "I'd rather have law than people."

Morris gave him what solace he could and went away. He didn't try to make an occasion of his coming or to find subjects of conversation, for he realized what it was that Roger got from him and knew that it had no dependence on time or words. He was the last sure hold that Roger had on life, the one he needed if he was to leave it with some sense of integrity and direction. Otherwise he would have gone to his death as if he were a mosquito or a snake, a thing pursued and trapped and struck at. Morris felt upheld by the boy's need of him and knew that he must see him through and do out the duty.

Artema again took down the arguments at the hearing before the Pardon Board and they were filed away. The application being for clemency and not for considerations of law, the lawyers spoke directly on personal grounds, and Moulder outdid himself in his eagerness to present the crime as the most sordid of the century and the execution as the most clearly justified in the name of law and order. The Pardon Board was not slow to agree with him, and on December 1 only the Governor stood between Roger and the chair.

With his transfer to the immediate death cell, life took on a new dimension. While Roger had had small confidence in the Supreme Court, the Pardon Board, and the Governor, they did stand between him and death and diluted the idea of it. It was as if the veil had not yet been lifted from the dread finality, which was less dreadful, because less imminent, so long as the veil was still in place. He could look past it and around it. His gaze was not yet fully riveted upon it. The hooded thing took a cold step closer when the Supreme Court affirmed the sentence, and another when the Pardon Board refused his application. It was directly before him now, still veiled but close, and waiting.

Roger's last days were a fight against terror. He had few resources to oppose to it, but his very helplessness and weakness, which had deserted Bellz, partly steadied him. He wished for Pengo's bravado, but that had been overdone. If the extreme penalty is ever to serve mankind, its victims must reach death just spent and unarmed: the arc of their lives must touch the neuter line precisely at the electric chair, when for an instant they are as they were at birth. Thus helpless, they might touch the public conscience. Most likely it has never happened, but it almost did in Roger, although he was aware of nothing more than the need to keep his sanity. Otherwise, unknown waters would rise above his head, more fearful in their dark origins than the known processes of man.

The struggle gave him a waxlike transparency. His eyes grew enormous as his body shrank to barely a hundred and ten pounds. He ate little. He would fasten his gaze upon the black door across the forecourt and feel a hard comfort from it. He was being rolled about in the bottom of the barrel of the world's cruelties, and it was a relative struggle between the rising flood of mindlessness and the gross clarity of the chair. Between these two cold destinies, the more familiar brought a perverse salvation. He recoiled from losing control: the loss of conscious life seemed better. For a time it lifted his mind from the grinding crush of death and made the whole business an exercise in choice.

He was not allowed to rest long on this artificial shelf of security. He was told of the action of the Pardon Board, and the last week began. On Sunday the Warden fixed Tuesday as the date, at twelve thirty past midnight, and informed Roger. The Governor had gone on vacation on Saturday, leaving word behind him that he would not stop the wheels of justice. He went to the Caribbean and took to a sailboat which had no ship-to-shore telephone. Morris could not personally afford to hire planes to search for him, and the County Treasury would not allow such an expense. Even had he been able to reach the Governor, he had no hope that he could move him to leniency.

As it was, Morris spent Monday and the rest of his fee telephoning to strategic ports where the Governor might have put in, but to no avail, and the Lieutenant-Governor, in view of the Governor's message, refused to act. By six o'clock he gave up, and he and Artema got into their car and headed for the prison. Leaving her at the inn in the town, Morris reached the death house at about ten o'clock and learned that no further visits were allowed after that hour. The prisoner was supposed to have uninterrupted spiritual instruction from the chaplain. Somehow he had to let Roger know that he had kept his promise and was there.

*   *   *

The Governor no longer stood between Roger and death. The Warden had told him at six o'clock that there was no hope of reprieve.

The black door was the only barrier left. Nothing prevented its opening for him except the intervening time.

He had felt no real hope all day Monday. Never had time gone so slowly, but the deadly march of the hours brought a kind of numbness, a hypnotic suspension which he had not felt at any time before. He tried to sleep, but could do no more than look mistily at the wall through half-closed eyes. At noon the Warden tested the reserve generators: the light outside the cells dimmed a little, a faint hum was audible, and the building shook gently. For the first time Roger went cold with fear and felt as if his heart would burst with pounding.

He fought his way back to some degree of stability, but he had begun to tremble and could not stop. The chaplain came and went, but Roger had had no religion in his life and soon lost the thread of what the chaplain was saying. It was too hard for him. There was too much else pressing in upon him. He became passive, and the chaplain went away. He had little to hold on to outside himself, except Morris, and he wondered if the lawyer was coming. He knew what Morris was doing today, but believed that he would come at last. All that he needed was to make contact once more and to know that Morris was there at the end: it would help him to hold up. He refused his supper.

He sat on his bed and watched the last daylight he would ever see drain from the sky. When the window was at last dark there was nothing left to take his attention but the black door. He eyed it with increasing fright and suddenly went utterly to pieces. His legs would not support him, and he fell on his bed with racking dry sobs. He would not see light again. The mean things in his cell at once became dear to him. He would live with them forever if they would let him stay and be faithful to his chair and table and bed and barred door. He would learn to live with them and love them. He could not think of leaving them and never coming back. The terror rose in his chest.

At about nine o'clock the official executioner tested the generators again. This time Roger sat and shook in abject misery and fear. If only death might come unexpectedly. Waiting for a set hour gave the situation an air of hideous formality and deliberation that was torture.

At ten o'clock the guard brought him word that Morris had arrived, but when Roger asked eagerly to see him, he was told that no further visits were allowed. He could not understand the implications of this. Surely his lawyer could come, but if he had to send word of his arrival, it must mean that he could not do more, not even enter through the black door and be with him in the room. That was where his presence would count. Roger was in torment and poured it out to the chaplain when he came again, but the chaplain only shook his head mournfully and said that there was nothing he could do. The guard refused to take a message to the Warden.

Roger fell into a stupor. The arc of his life was plunging downward. His spirit was already well on its way, and only mind and body remained to withstand the final mechanics of dissolution. His mind could not stop trying to pierce the dark and discover what tomorrow would be like for him. His body could not stop trembling. He was so weak that he could barely stand.

At midnight the guard rolled the screen down the corridor until it stood between him and the black door. It was about seven feet high, and he could hear the shuffling feet of the witnesses entering the forecourt. Then there was a new glow: the black door opened to let them enter the death room, and closed behind them. He wanted to call out Morris's name, but his mouth was dry and he could utter no sound. There was no word for him either, and his spirit sank to its lowest point. He had been abandoned.

The screen was rolled back.

At twelve twenty-five they came for him. Well used

to the routine, the chaplain rose and held out the cross
to Roger, who convulsively grasped it and the chaplain's hand together, less in religious fervor than for
support.

The guards told him to step one pace beyond his cell
door. As he did so they swiftly slit his trousers from the
knee down and undid the top buttons of his shirt.

The chaplain stepped slowly forward, repeating the
Twenty-third Psalm in a low voice and holding Roger's
frail weight with the cross between their hands. The
guards fell in beside the boy, hands near his body but
not touching him. He was to walk alone if he could.

He just managed to. His heart was thundering in his
chest and he was shaking, but he walked slowly and
painfully, as if in fever. They halted before the black
door, to let it open.

And then the veil was lifted. Nothing but twelve feet
of space stood between Roger and the end of life.

His gaze was now fully riveted. Facing the door, ten
feet beyond it, stood the electric chair. Above it was a
ventilator of the kind that carries off smoke and fumes.
Within the ventilator was a light. The rest of the room
was in darkness, but the light, like an ugly yellow lily
upside down, showed each detail of the waiting chair.
Its arms, stretched toward him, were extra long, its back
was extra high, and it was made of bare wood. At calf

height and at wrist points were the electrodes. At the top of the back hung the heavy leather mask with wires leading into it like the snakes in the head of Medusa. In an alcove behind the chair stood the executioner by his panel of controls and indicators. The charge would be two thousand volts, the amperage twelve. The Warden stood beside the chair.

The air was dead and flat, and nothing stirred but Roger's slow, half-creeping march into the room. He had paused on the threshold with a little gasp when he first saw the chair, and the guards had gently urged him forward. He reached it now and paused to turn around.

"Have you any last request?" the Warden asked.

Roger's eyes darted about. He couldn't see into the darkened room from within the circle of light. "Mr. Longa?" he asked timidly.

"I'm here, Roger." Morris's voice came distinctly from the shadow, and the Warden looked up angrily. The rule was silence, and Morris had not dared to speak before, in fear of being excluded or even ejected from the room. But now he spoke in answer to the boy's question. A light jumped into Roger's eyes and a faint smile crossed his face.

"Mr. Longa," he managed to whisper, looking in the direction of the voice. "Thanks for everything."

He started, painfully and uncertainly, to lower himself into the chair, but now the guards were swift. They lifted him deep into the seat and adjusted the electrodes at calves and wrists.

Then they fastened a thick belt across his chest and lowered over his head the heavy wired leather mask.

It hid all but the tip of his nose and his lips. He was making efforts to quiet them by biting his tongue, the best that he could do, against his racing mind and heart, to keep control and to sit erect for Morris to see.

The guards stepped back. The Warden, who had stood by with arm raised, lowered his hand. It had taken a minute and thirty-seven seconds.

There was a low whine and a short loud snap, as of huge teeth closing.

Roger's head flew back and his body leaped forward against the confining straps. Almost at once smoke arose from his head and left wrist and was sucked up into the ventilator overhead. The body churned against the bonds, the lips ceased trembling and turned red, then slowly changed to blue. Moisture appeared on the skin and a sizzling noise was audible. The smell of burning flesh grew heavy in the air.

Roger was being broiled.

The current went off with a distinct clap after about two minutes and Roger slumped back in his seat, his head hanging. No one moved. Then came the second jolt and again the body surged against the restraining straps and smoke rose from it. The visible flesh was turkey red.

Again the current slammed off and this time the doctor stepped forward to listen, but he moved back again and shook his head. Apparently Roger still clung faintly to life.

The third charge struck him, and again the smoking and sizzling and broiling. His flesh was swelling around the straps.

The doctor listened carefully and raised his head.

"I pronounce this man dead," he said, folding up his stethoscope. It was seven minutes after Roger had been seated in the chair.

The guards came forward and undid the straps. As they lifted off the heavy leather mask the tip of Roger's tongue fell out and the corners of his mouth were visibly bloody. One eye was closed, the other glared forth. One of the guards wheeled out a table, and Roger's body was dumped on it. It was taken for an immediate autopsy, including the modern version of driving a stake through its heart, which now was removed from the body and then replaced and the opening sewed up.

Outside of the walls there was a small cemetery where unclaimed bodies of electrocuted felons were buried.

His grave already prepared, Roger was put in it before dawn.

It was there, under a few blowing trees that looked out upon the quiet farms and woodlands, that Roger met the light of the new day.

Comment

I PROTEST this dreadful case.

Punitive penology has failed utterly. Society could have made better use of Roger Haike than turning him into fertilizer. Its vengeance does not save souls, restore minds, or mend consciences.

Walls, tommy-guns, searchlights, bars, and repression do not work, and the sixty-per-cent recidivist rate is proof that they do not.

There is a mighty difference between a man's first and second offenses. Both the offender and society may be judged tolerantly when his first offense occurs, for there are a thousand subtle factors at work upon us all. But one part of society may not take refuge behind the facile solution that all we need to do to prevent crime is to make better people. Nor should the other part of society feel that the only solution is to cage and punish. The first offense should be regarded as a regrettable happening. Once it has been committed, devices should be applied so accurate and sure that it will not be repeated.

The incorrigibles must be held, perhaps indefinitely, as a monument to our lack of wisdom. The rest must be treated, with an individual solution for each.

And no one killed, for we never know about the strange working of God's grace, and we should not waste human material or assume it damned.

A word must be said about the causes of crime and juvenile delinquency.

Causes of anything can be listed on a piece of paper, but unless crime is related to place and circumstance and time, a list is of little worth. Crime is something that is the matter with people, as law is something with which people try to stop or cure the ill. Both forces operate in depth, three-dimensionally.

Crime is a disease of civilization. It is not an inevitable part of human nature. It can be studied and improved in the way that civilization can be studied and improved.

The causes of crime are: (1) failure by the police and the Courts to solve, by capture and conviction, more than one crime in five; (2) liquor; (3) broken, severe, neglectful, and unsympathetic homes; (4) social weaknesses, such as poverty and the mass media like motion pictures, television, and publications that offer shows of crime and violence; (5) special reasons, such as the need of money for food, doctors, rent, and the like.

Unwise legislation is a sixth cause. In Pennsylvania, for instance, horse racing and taking bets on it are illegal, but they are legal in every bordering State and there are six of them: Ohio, New York, New Jersey, Delaware, Maryland, and West Virginia. This kind of situation brings the law into disrespect.

The last cause is our vindictive penal system, the thing this book is written to attack.

These causes are constant, but they mean little unless related to city or country, economic feast or famine, war or peace, and a host of other factors, great and small.

For juveniles, one of the many factors not named above must be moved up almost to top position—idleness. Adults forget the time scale: five minutes to an adult is an hour to a juvenile. Another difficulty is that criminal behavior has less to do with good and evil in a juvenile mind than it has in an adult mind. The *codex criminalis* was written by adults at an adult moral level and on an adult time scale. People are born good but must learn evil, and the criminal business, pro or contra, is a matter of education. The trouble is that education contra stops too soon. The crime rate drops off at age twenty-five: formal education stops at eighteen, except for those that can go to college. That there is a direct relation between education and crime is shown by the relatively few college-educated people who commit crime.

Man turns a corner at twenty-five: that is, he matures at twenty-five and not before. Until then he can and should be considered a potential killer, raper, and thief, if he has as little as five minutes in which to grow bored and make the wrong choice. After twenty-five, society can safely take a chance on him. Before twenty-five, society can trust him all the way, provided it keeps him constantly busy. Every minute of a juvenile's time should be filled.

Society, however, allows a seven-year gap between the crucial ages of eighteen and twenty-five, a period in which major things happen to a youth: he may drive a car, he may marry, he comes of age, he starts to work. A wrong step in any one of these important affairs, even if accidental, may throw his whole life out of joint. Never again will he meet such formidable issues, but all that society offers him during these seven incandescent years is the police station and the prison.

One college, one loving home, one enlightened friend

or counselor, one instrument to combat idleness, one good Crime Prevention Association is worth a dozen police stations. Unless these "home remedies" are effectively encouraged and maintained on a wide scale, the shaking of graybeard heads and the fulminations of a sensation-hungry press mean nothing. And when the inevitable crime still occurs and the lawbreaker is taken, a new conception of penology must take hold in order to prevent a repetition and to protect society.

To protect society is the key. Matthew Hale, Lord Chief Justice of England in the time of Charles II, laid down Rules for Judicial Conduct, this among them:

"That in Business Capital [which was most of business criminal in his day], though my Nature prompt me to Pity, yet to consider there is also a Pity due the Country."

The poor make up the great bulk of the prison population, not only the poor in wealth but in intelligence and education and opportunity. The average IQ of our country's prisoners is 79, which is not far above moron level; their average education is eighth grade; their average crimes are theft and assault; they commit most of their crimes between the ages of twenty and twenty-five; and they come from the lowest income levels.

Judges are constantly being told by police who cannot

or will not catch the prime felons to be severe with the small criminal because he will lead to the big one. The Little Man, despite the pratings of democracy, is still the scapegoat.

We catch the lawbreakers who are poor in intellectual and material means and cannot manage to get away. But we do not catch all of our criminals. Most of them walk the streets undetected, but the hinges of society do not fall off on that account. We spend time and money on prisoners who need little or no correction and not enough on those that do. We know that about a million and a half people pass through our jails and prisons each year for big and little offenses, and they are a minority of our criminals. In 1956, returns from 1,771 urban communities showed that twenty-eight and a half per cent of all reported crimes were solved by arrest. It would certainly be conservative to say that twenty per cent were not only arrested but convicted and punished as well, and it is impossible to say how many crimes were unreported. This should give us an uncomfortable feeling about the guests at dinner. About one person in thirty-five must be an uncaught criminal.

When the average man breaks the law his reactions are apt to be one of two kinds. Either he is so thankful for not being caught that he tells no one but decides never to repeat the offense, and he does not. Or he is so shaken by what he did that he confesses, and the purgative quality of confession takes one of two forms: either he throws himself on the known mercy of his friends or parents and is not punished because he was honest, or, if his friends or parents are the State and the Judge, he clears his soul and takes his punishment. How sweet are the uses of confession! If it were not for the awful urge to clear one's conscience and plead guilty, we would not solve a tenth of the crimes that we do.

Since man first walked upright, his fellows have taken advantage of these mercies. My real subject is man's inhumanity to man. For there is a third reaction to crime, that of the few wicked and of the many ill of soul, and our punishments have been made with them in view. This is the kink in the problem: the guilty innocents, the toe-stubbers, the pure in heart who have done wrong but who can still attain a state of grace. These serve the sentences of the few unholy ones.

Our punishments are written for the worst offenders and we are not yet wise enough to do better or even well by them. Let us no longer treat the lesser offenders in terms of the worst, even when we extend leniency, and let us have done with vengeance.

The State has been given the right to commit various of the crimes it outlaws. It may murder, steal, entrap, and assault. It murders murderers; it confiscates not only contraband but the vehicle in which the contraband is carried; it entraps by tapping wires and using informers; it assaults by whatever force is needed to arrest and subdue. These things are done in the cause of law and order, but there is something amiss when evil must be corrected by duplicating it.

The State may duplicate the crime of false imprisonment.

The crime of imprisonment might be the title of these pages, as it is the title of one of Shaw's most searching and most scathing polemics. The State may commit these crimes, not because it must do so to keep the peace but because the men and women who run the State are not yet wise enough to create better solutions. Until we are wiser we will go on killing and caging our fellow men, and that is where modern psychiatry, psychology, sociology, and medicine must come in.

The argument is often made that reform is sentimental. This is the theme of the most bloodthirsty among us who imagine that prisoners are coddled because they get steak once a month and movies twice a week and that this is wrong, prison and even hanging being too good for the likes of them.

As any level-headed philosopher will agree, hatred and malice and vengeance are the worst forms of sentimentality. It is Shaw's argument that we are grossly sentimental about the people we choose to murder legally. It cannot be the insane: it must be the sane. What perversion of common sense is this? So long as we permit the death penalty at all, let us kill off the right people, the homicidal maniacs and the insane killers. We need not do it vengefully or in bad blood, but rather with relief, once they have been determined to be fit candidates for the gas chamber or the electric chair. Then let us quietly, dispassionately, painlessly, even apologetically return them to Mother Earth. It is the sane killers that should give us pause. Most of them will never take life again, for a man does not realize what a fearful thing it is to murder until he has done it. The average murderer is far less a continuing social menace than the professional thief.

Capital punishment is at present at a low ebb, for juries are assigning it only in the most lurid cases. The national yearly total has fallen from a hundred and fifty to about seventy in the past ten years, and such a small number has no deterrent effect whatever. With people being executed at the rate of less than two in each State each year, no one is deterred from murder by the thought that it might happen to him. Every killer knows that juries hunt for excuses to avoid the death penalty, and it is not hard to provide a murder and a sort of reason too. After fifteen to eighteen years the Pardon Board will let him out. The death penalty has lost what little virtue as a deterrent it once may have had when criminals were massacred in impressive numbers: the seventy murderers who were electrocuted last year have not deterred the seventy who are being electrocuted this year. England, in the days of Lord Coke, hanged eight hundred persons per year, but killing so many could not have had much effect either, or the annual number would have been less. The argument for taking life seems to fail both ways.

The proponents of capital punishment argue that even if it is rarely used, its presence on the statute books is a potent factor in deterrence. Its history does not bear this out, for the retention or abolition of the supreme penalty seems to have little effect on the murder rate in those States that have experimented with abolition. If anything, the rate is slightly less in the abolition States. Seven States have abolished it, and six others abolished it for a while and then went back to it. Thirty-six nations have no capital punishment for murder, although they retain it for treason, excepting only Uruguay, Western Germany, and San Marino.

The supreme penalty gathers health from its sentimental enemies and from strong but irrelevant arguments against it. It is of course true that we take upon ourselves the role of the Almighty when we take life and that if we make a mistake there is no way to correct it.

It is odd about the Sixth Commandment. People apply it only to the defendant, not to the State. They interpret it to read: "Thou shalt not kill, except those who have killed others," or: "Thou shalt not kill save by due process of law."

The Sixth Commandment consists of four words and no exceptions, not even self-defense: Jesus did not try to save His life by defending it. The Commandment reads: "Thou shalt not kill." This is the wording of the King James and Douai versions of the Bible. The original Old Testament word was "murder," which can be argued to apply only to the citizen and not to the State or Sovereign, but our Anglo-Saxon law grew up under the King James language. However primitive the Mosaic law may have been, Jesus' position on the death penalty is expressed in the story of the woman who was taken in adultery, an offense punishable by stoning to death, when He said that the first stone should be cast by him who was without sin.

The Seventh Commandment is not interpreted: "Thou shalt not commit adultery except with those who have themselves committed adultery." Maybe those who commit adultery say just that and ascribe it to the weakness of human nature. But one cannot ascribe to human weakness the calculated killing of a human being by the State.

Strong as these considerations are, they are not the sort that move people: pure Christian doctrine seldom does, except in church. People love to think that the worst they can do is not enough to stop an evil which they are not sure they want to stop anyway, and hence the horror of their worst behavior is the very thing that convinces them they should go on with it.

It is strange how people talk about deterrence and the death penalty. Great publicity is given to war and its horrors under pious captions that knowledge of its horror may deter the race from future wars. But no publicity is given to executions, though the argument for deterrence is the same. Why not show executions in motion pictures, television, stage, and press, so that all may see, if they have such magnificent deterring power? Why is the State so ashamed of its process that it must kill at dead of night, in an isolated place, and on an unnamed day?

A great deal of nonsense is written about the death penalty. Among the worst is the suggestion that life imprisonment is preferable, since there is hope while there is life.

If life imprisonment literally meant the full remainder of a man's years spent behind prison walls, most convicts would welcome the electric chair. What exquisite torture it must be to know that there is no hope of release or of personal development in a normal human environment! True life imprisonment is a ghastly and terrible thing, as can be seen in the accounts of it by men who have served thirty or forty years.

The reason there is no outcry about it is that a sentence of life imprisonment is hypocritical and does not mean what it says. Pardon Boards are releasing prisoners all the time, and the average life sentence ranges between ten and eighteen years. The integrity and dignity of the law suffer from being made to mouth sentences that do not mean what they say.

There is a point of no return in serving time. Beyond it a man goes downhill past redemption and might as well have been killed in the first place. I set fifteen years as the outer limit of possible reform from time alone, and far less, except for the mad dogs, from intelligent treatment. Why keep the longer and more costly method?

Even after fifteen years the world can seem a new and sinister place to the man who is given a suit of clothes and a ten-dollar bill and is pushed out of the jailhouse door. Men have fainted or have tried to flee back into the security of custody. The street seems a mile wide and they have become helpless to do the simplest things: they have forgotten that doors have knobs, that change should be counted, that they need not ask permission for each step they take or, which is worse, that there is no one to ask. Many men soon commit new crimes, not because they are incorrigible but because the transition from full custody to no custody has been too abrupt and because if a man has for years led the abnormal life of prison he may be expected, having no adequate standards of behavior, to compensate by living abnormally when he is released. And a man learns fear when there is no one to turn to.

Society is even apt to impose a dead hand. If an articulate inmate like Nathan Leopold wants to tell the paralyzing story of punitive penology, he is likely to be told: "Who wants to know what you know?"

In its right perspective capital punishment should be regarded not as a solitary evil but only as the most dramatic form of a more general evil, that of punishment. Punishment, not capital punishment alone, is the enemy.

Let us turn our guns on punishment itself. Until the Quakers set up the Walnut Street jail in Philadelphia in 1790, prisons were not used as a method of punishing criminals. Debtors, political prisoners, and some slaves were imprisoned, but for ordinary criminal offenses the correctives were death, exile, and torture. Prisons were used in England as houses of detention for persons awaiting trial at the quarterly assizes, and the trials emptied the jails.

Less than a hundred and fifty years ago England had over two hundred offenses punishable by death, including stealing a lace handkerchief worth five shillings and shooting the King's deer. In the Middle Ages society had a considerable catalogue of tortures, including the Iron Maiden, drawing and quartering, breaking on the wheel, bone-crushing, tongue-extraction, blinding, flesh-ripping, nail-pulling, burning at the stake, crushing by increasing weights, smothering in ashes, strangulation by water, smearing with honey and spread-eagling over red ants' nests, hanging by the thumbs, flaying, burying alive, exposure to wild animals, and so on. King Edward II of England was killed in a way that was intended to leave no obvious mark upon his skin. His bowels were burned out by red-hot irons passed into his body through the anus.

This was the sentence that was passed on Sir Walter Raleigh in 1603, following his conviction for treason: "That you shall be had from hence to the place whence you came, there to remain until the day of execution. And from thence you shall be drawn upon a hurdle through the open streets to the place of execution, there to be hanged and cut down alive, and your privy members cut off and thrown into the fire before your eyes, and your body shall be opened, your heart and bowels plucked out. Then your head to be stricken off from your body, and your body shall be divided into four quarters, to be disposed of at the King's pleasure. And God have mercy upon your soul."

Man has been singularly inventive in devising discomfort for his fellows. The Oriental lexicon of torture is beyond all praise for ingenuity. It was a great step forward when capital punishment was limited to the gibbet, the broadsword, and the guillotine.

The 1790 Quakers took the revolutionary step of using their jails as places of punishment, with hard labor to make healthy bodies and separate and solitary confinement to make healthy minds, and also reduced the number of capital offenses to the single one of first-degree murder. Voltaire and other liberals in Europe hailed it with a great shout. But in 1842 Charles Dickens was writing very differently, in his *American Notes*, after visiting the Eastern Penitentiary, which is still in use in Philadelphia. He wrote of the sailor who had been shut up alone for eleven years, speaking to no one and seeing no face but that of the guard who brought his meals, and who did nothing, even under Dickens's kindly questioning, but keep his head down and pick at the flesh upon his fingers. I like to think that Dickens was looking across the years at us when he wrote: "I am the more convinced that here there is a depth of terrible endurance which none but the sufferers themselves can fathom and which no man has a right to inflict upon his fellow-creature. I hold this slow and daily tampering with the mysteries of the brain to be immeasurably worse than any torture of the body: and because its ghastly signs and tokens are not so palpable to the eye and sense of touch as scars upon the flesh; because its wounds are not upon the surface, and it extorts few cries that human ears can hear; therefore I the more denounce it, as a secret punishment which slumbering humanity is not roused up to stay."

Solitary confinement is gone now. Inmates may visit each other, play games, and enjoy magazines, newspapers, books, radio, movies, and correspondence courses. But they all want to get out. Any restriction of freedom, even under enlightened conditions of penology, feels like punishment. Facile reformers must realize that it is as hard to convince prisoners that punishment is a sin as it is to convince the public. Often it is the one tangible thing they can hold on to, the debt that they must pay to society and the receipt that society is supposed to give to them in return. Unfortunately, society is loath to give a receipt in full, but goes on exacting punishment in terms of suspicion, references refused, jobs denied, confidence withheld. Usually a man finds that his real punishment does not begin until after his release from prison. We have, as was said above, about sixty per cent repeaters in our prisons. Something is wrong. If people are treated like animals they will behave like animals and vengeance will be repaid by vengeance. It is hard to change an inmate's idea about that.

Penology is the fertile field in which to plant new ideas about crime and to put psychiatry to work. Much is going on there and much has taken shape. There are three main developments.

First, the parole administration is beginning to share with the judge, and, in the case of the longer sentences, is taking over altogether the responsibility for determining the duration of confinement beyond the minimum. The decision rests partly on the prisoner's sentence and partly on his progress. Modern legislation and projected model acts like that of the American Law Institute, now being written, provide for elastic sentences with adjustable minima and long maxima and for initial classification immediately following sentence to a diagnostic center. The power to sentence is not being taken wholly from the judge, nor should it be until our penological procedures are farther advanced. It is still important, in order to slake the public's sense of justice, that it be able to see its avenger sitting in the flesh upon the seat of judgment. The fully indeterminate sentence may drive a prisoner mad. He is willing to work for his freedom by good behavior, but he must have some way of figuring when he will get out.

The second trend is toward a greater range of penal institutions within each State, from the fortress type like Alcatraz to a new type of minimum-security prison or even a completely open farm or forestry camp. This must be the path of future development. Modern theory is that only ten to twenty-five per cent of our prisoners need maximum security: they are the ones whose condition we are not yet wise enough to improve. Another twenty-five per cent need no security at all, but do need guidance and training. The remainder need intermediate or symbolic restraint and considerable educative guidance, which should extend into effective probationary supervision after release. In institutions of the minimum or open type the repeater rate has dropped abruptly, sometimes as much as from sixty to five per cent.

Finally, modern penology envisages training and guidance by way of teaching, whether educative or vocational, with the objective held clearly before each inmate that he is not merely being held in but is being prepared for the world when he is let out. When that objective can be achieved he will feel differently about punishment. He will not see restraint as a frustrating battle with the calendar, but as a training program whose aim is his ultimate benefit. These are the law's green pastures for the psychiatrist, and he is taking hold with vigor and effect. His effort is to make the punishment fit the prisoner and to swing the penal purpose the whole way over from vengeance to treatment and education. When he has his procedures working, it should not take the public long to follow, as it is their friends and relations that are directly affected.

Penology is beginning to regard criminals as ill men. The more horrible the crime, the greater may be the criminal's deviation from mankind's moderate average madness and the more help he should have, provided we have it to give. A case in point is that of John Gilbert Graham, who tried to collect his mother's insurance by stowing a bomb into the airplane in which she and forty-three other people were traveling. He was found legally sane under the M'Naghten Rule and gassed, but it is hard to believe that anyone who would do such a thing was not emotionally twisted almost beyond repair. Prob-

ably we have nothing for him in our social pharmaco-
poeia and he was the best type to kill so long as we are
going to kill anybody.

When we talk of moral illness as a moving cause of
crime, we must stop and think a bit. Remember Shaw's
parallel between crime and tuberculosis. "Why a man
who is punished," he wrote, "for having an inefficient
conscience should be privileged to have an inefficient
lung is a debatable question. If one is sent to prison and
the other to hospital, why make the prison so different
from the hospital?"

In Samuel Butler's *Erewhon* the ideas of disease and
crime are reversed. If a man broke into another's house
and stole, his family and friends gathered around him to
commiserate and express the hope that he would soon
recover from his regrettable attack of burglary. But if he
developed a stomach ache he was looked at with suspicion and clapped into jail. There is a charming incident
of an Erewhonian judge sentencing a man for tuberculosis: he read the criminal record of the accused, starting
with the common cold and working up through grippe
and influenza to pulmonary pneumonia. He then read
the wretched defendant a terrible lecture and gave him
a severe sentence.

It is not quite so mad as it sounds. If we do not imprison those that are sick in body, why do we imprison

those that are sick in conscience? And except for the mad dogs, I am not convinced that society would fall apart if, since we do not punish the medically ill, we did not punish the criminally ill at all. Hospital patients are to a degree imprisoned, but they do not feel punished on that account, and the criminal should not feel so if he also received the kind of therapy that fits his case. Since the hospital patient does not think of his period of detention in terms of imprisonment, it is likely that in the penology of the future the criminal patient will not either.

There are a few things to be remembered about punishment. At the top of the list is the idea that the protection of society from further crime is the only intelligent approach. Vengeance will get us nowhere, because, like war, it begets only more vengeance. This is a mature idea and not easy to achieve, as we may have to watch with acquiescence the murderer of a child, perhaps our own, go lightly punished. It is an unsentimental idea, as it calls upon us also to admit that life or destroyed property cannot be restored, no matter how much vengeance is wreaked, and hence that we may as well take the one road that will protect us against repetitions: this may involve special, thoughtful, and even lenient handling. The worse a man's behavior, the more must be done for him to set him straight; and the more that is done for him, the more likely he will be to respond to it.

The next consideration is that the punishment of the future, though it be called punishment because it entails loss of freedom, will feel more like treatment and education. The sting will be gone from it because its whole effort will be directed toward making each inmate who will yield to treatment a socially useful person. Upon his release, he will no longer feel that the hand of society is against him.

Next, we must accept the fact that others are not deterred from crime by the severity of punishment, but only by its certainty. The severity of a sanction makes its certainty less certain: witnesses fail to testify, juries refuse to convict. In England, with its ocean barriers and its relatively homogeneous population, capture is reasonably certain and prison sentences are materially shorter than here. But if a man knows, as he does in this country, that he has eight chances in ten to evade the penalty of the law, he will run those chances no matter how severe the penalty may be. A change from severe to more lenient criminal laws has usually resulted in a decrease in the crime rate.

Further, it is easy to forget how coarse a compromise our trial procedures and our criminal laws are. The trial produces a result which may be consistent with the obvious facts and yet may have little to do with the facts of personality and individual purpose. It becomes of enormous importance that a man be handled following conviction with more regard for the integrity of his personality than for the integrity of a padlock. Having subordinated man to a system, during his arrest and trial, we can achieve balance only by subordinating the system to the man thereafter and by handling him with all our subtlety and knowledge.

Small things matter largely. A man may be charged with twenty-one robberies and may plead guilty to twenty of them, and the maximum penalty may total two hundred years, but if he did not commit the twenty-first and is found guilty of it, he will be filled with a flaming sense of injustice. Ignominy thirsts for what respect it can find, and if you do not understand this, go and visit a prison and think about self-respect as you walk through the stony corridors and see the faces of the men.

Again, do not be deceived by the easy statement that crime does not pay. Organized crime, such as lottery, prostitution, narcotics, gambling, and skillfully planned theft, pays very handsomely indeed. In the crimes that arise from the social appetites the risks are not great, for the laws against the pleasurable human weaknesses are only sporadically enforced, the take is high, and a spot of time in prison now and then is suffered as an occupational risk. It is also well known how to cut one's time to the minimum by being a model prisoner.

Less obvious is the fact that punishment does not pay. It clearly does not, with sixty per cent of our prisoners. And, as I have pointed out above, it may be unwise even to determine the guilt or innocence of a man whose driving impulse is to enjoy punishment, or to accept in all cases a man's confession of his guilt, or to overload those sensitive consciences that are capable of punishing themselves.

Finally, the wrong penalty may be given to a properly guilty man who should suffer a social sanction. The whole value of apprehension and trial can be made or broken at this last stage, for capture and conviction are preliminaries. The ax falls only when sentence is passed: society's punishment does not begin until then.

Psychiatry should not be heard until the time has come for punishment to take direct effect. Then let the doctors concentrate their forces and make their full effort. M'Naghten will have been left behind. The psychiatrist will no longer be subject to public embarrassment in Court. Much can be done to restore the psychiatrically innocent man who has been found legally guilty. This is the point at which to place the fulcrum that will oust M'Naghten and with him the punitive nature of our penal system. I am confident, as I said above, that the public can be made to think differently about crime and punishment when it sees its own people emerge from prison improved and better equipped for living. One result of the present system is to make people feel that if a man leaves prison better than he was when he entered it, it was not because of what he found there but in spite of it. Tragically enough, this feeds the sadism in man and makes him approve of retribution all the more.

If anyone doubts that punishment by imprisonment is vengeful, let him consider what is done to the prisoners who break the rules and are disciplined within the institution. The effort is to break their spirit by direct retaliation. The offender is put in separate and solitary confinement. In the Illinois prison where Nathan Leopold [1] served thirty-three and a half years this was called The Hole. There was nothing in it but a small high window covered by a heavy mesh, a shelf built out from the concrete wall to sleep on, and a bucket. The cell had an outer solid steel door with a chuckhole in it and an inner barred door inches inside it. The prisoner had one large slice of bread and a cup of water each day, and he was handcuffed to the barred door for twelve hours out of

[1] See Nathan F. Leopold: *Life Plus 99 Years* (New York: Doubleday and Company; 1958).

the twenty-four. He faced the solid door and had to stand. When night came the cell was completely dark. In another prison the solitary cells had no window and no bench. Men spent up to sixty days in such places.

It is no far step from this to the prison guards in Philadelphia who on a hot summer day locked a group of recalcitrants in Klondike, a separate-punishment room provided with excessive steam pipes, and turned on the steam. Four prisoners died. The guards were convicted of manslaughter.

This sort of thing is expected to turn prisoners into useful citizens.

Let the doubters also take stock of the tragic confusion of the prosecutor who in 1953 opposed the release of Nathan Leopold on parole. Leopold wrote that he "made a scathing speech in which he said that I should have been executed. Since I had not been, I must certainly be kept in prison all my life as an example to others. . . . He admitted freely that he was convinced that I was rehabilitated and that my release would not endanger society. But this, he said, was irrelevant. My case had become a symbol. The rights of society transcended any personal rights I might have. If I were released, all judges in the future, when confronted with a case similar to mine, would be afraid to sentence the defendant to life: they would have to order his execution."

The absurdity of these extraordinary statements should be apparent on their face.

In what kind of institution might the new ideas be seen at work?

About thirty miles east of Pasadena there is a small town called Chino, and within its boundaries there is located the California Institution for Men. It is not even called a prison. It lies in a region of rich farmland against a background of mountains. In the foreground some twenty-five hundred acres have been fenced about with barbed wire, to keep cattle in or out, as the case might be. There is a gate and a gatehouse, a simple swinging gate which can be locked at night as a man might lock his front door to keep out thieves and prowlers, but certainly not to keep them in. There are drives flanked with trees, several hundreds of acres of truck gardens, and fields where cattle graze. There are buildings whose doors are not locked at night, and several thousand men sleep there, but there are no cells or barred gates and most of the men live alone in small neat rooms. In other buildings there are vocational projects where trades and occupations are taught, and when a man leaves the institution he goes to a specific job as well. Each man does a full day's work raising the institution's food or learning a trade or working in the hills. There are no armed guards, no lookout towers, no searchlights.

There is a gymnasium, a swimming-pool built by the men, a library where no class of books is forbidden and where art exhibits are shown, including the work of any talented inmate. There is an area of trees and garden with lawn furniture, and once a week the families of the inmates may come to visit and find their men not in uniform but in their ordinary civilian clothes. Visiting privileges last four hours on these Sunday afternoons, and no man is shamed before his children.

One third of the population is not even inside the barbed-wire fence but out in the hills working in the forests or on the firebrakes. Shortly before their release men who need it are given lessons in conventional etiquette or are shown the latest developments in the world outside, if they have been away a long time, and are taught how to cope with them. There are usually a few men whose release has been delayed for one reason or another and who feel depressed. When this has happened at Christmastime the Superintendent has opened his home to them, shared his turkey dinner, and sung carols with them around his piano and Christmas tree.

Chino began rather as a political accident and has succeeded beyond the expectation of its founders. It has a record of about six per cent repeaters and two to four per cent escapes, for freedom is a heady wine, even at Chino, but no one who escapes can ever go back there: he goes to San Quentin. One prisoner inadvertently released from a specialized hospital ahead of schedule walked back twenty-five miles to avoid being accused of trying to escape. Inmates returning late at night from a herding assignment in the hills have slept beside the gate until it opened in the morning.

The Chino escape percentage is high, compared with the rate for the fortress institutions whose main objective is to keep a locked door between a man and the street. Escapes from those are rare, and they may be serious if the fugitive is dangerous. At Chino, on the other hand, there should of course be no escapes and it is part of the program to talk the inmates out of wanting to walk away, but if they do go over the hill they are the least dangerous type of prisoner, or they would not be at Chino in the first place, and hence they present a minor threat to the neighbors. With so many hundreds of thousands of undetected criminals on the streets anyway, the few who take a walk from Chino do not add much danger to the public security. The threat of being returned to a fortress and not to Chino has in itself a considerable deterring effect.

The California institution is not unique. A few States

have similar ones, and the Federal prison system has its great open farm at Seagoville, Texas. England has its Ashwell, Holland its van der Hoeven Clinic. But they are still few, and every State should have its Chino.

The new current in penology faces four grave problems. One is the kind of penal structure we should have. We should not have to build many more of the fortress type where every inmate is constantly made aware that Big Brother is watching him so that he shall not get out and will kill him if he tries. As our general population expands, our prison population will expand with it and we shall need new penal structures. Let these be of the medium- and minimum-security or open-farm types. We can keep our fortresses to house the mad dogs.

Second, the repressed and abnormal emotional needs of prisoners must have constant attention and should be met by more imaginative devices than merely putting saltpeter in the food. The release of energy through work and study would help, as would more intelligent furlough and visiting privileges.

A third problem is the difficult one of prison labor. The unions show little disposition to allow prison labor to get into the market, but food-raising, farm labor, State work, and education can take up a great deal of slack if imaginatively applied.

Finally, it will be necessary to train guards especially for work in institutions like Chino. Political hacks let out to pasture will no longer do, nor will ignorant and suspicious men. Guards should be put under Civil Service, and the money we save by not building fortresses could be spent on personnel. The expansion is coming anyway and it may as well be directed intelligently.

Penology must be vastly simplified before it can become effective. At present it attempts to do too much: it tries to incarcerate, punish, deter, rehabilitate, and protect society, and of these the only one it succeeds in doing is to incarcerate.

Imprisonment should last for no longer or shorter time than is needed to make a man a socially useful person, regardless of what he has done. Why keep him in longer and waste the taxpayer's money? Because we hate him for what he once did? Vengeance is an expensive luxury. To hide a hateful man away or to punish him in public does not deter others. It once was that pickpockets were hanged in public on London's Tyburn Hill, but these ceremonies were discontinued because of the prevalence of pocket-picking at them.

The real agent of deterrence is the certainty of being caught. The trial may do little more than show others how to avoid capture.

The new penology need not scatter its fire in any such

way. To fit the penalty to the criminal means that the same penalty will not fit another criminal and hence that its whole deterring power will be conserved for the one for whom it was designed.

The main idea is that prisoners are people. We all want to commit crimes, or at least we all imagine doing so now and then, and the only real difference between a convict and a respectable citizen is that the one did and the other did not do the thing that they both at some time imagined doing. And of course the respectable citizen was not caught. How much real virtue is there in that? What kept the one from crossing the line and the other not? Can you be so very sure that only Virtue, with a capital V, is at work here?

There are many kinds of anti-social behavior, which we call crime: the kind that violates the person of another, like murder, rape, and assault, and so seems to violate some heavenly law of natural security; the kind that violates the property of another, a conception created less by God than by man; the kind that concerns the general public welfare, like the size of lobsters and the purity of food. These are subtle distinctions, and the human mind is prone to give them an order of importance based on their inherent nature. The true threat to society comes more from the inherent urge of a particular person to commit a crime of any sort than from the kind of crime that he does in fact commit.

In short, it is the single person that needs attention, not the single crime.

Our punishment must fit the person rather than his crime: this cannot be repeated too often.

If this central idea be accepted by the public, the new penology can advance broadly. Murderers may not go to jail at all. They may go for terms that are either short or long. Confirmed misdemeanants may go to jail for life. The feelings of the victims of a crime or of their relatives will be immaterial. Only the notion of remaking socially useful and criminally harmless citizens will be accepted as valid. Prisons will be more like colleges or vocational schools than jails. The best of care and treatment will be none too good for those whose crime betrays their need.

The aim will be to reduce recidivism from above sixty per cent to zero. Thus far the present system of retributive punishment has failed to do this.

The law should not presume to tell the doctors how to do their work. It has the right, however, to state the objective, which is the protection of society against repeated individual aggression. Only by achieving this can the law do its work economically and well. The process must not stop at the neuter point of rendering each prisoner harmless, but must also make him useful and achieve his rehabilitation. One element in this process is often overlooked, but the public will not overlook it, no matter what the system may be. It involves each prisoner's gaining such insight that he can face his crime squarely and condemn it or at least renounce the trail that led to it. The public will demand some evidence of his adequate and effective remorse. Men are not effectively punished by being beaten to their knees. The only real punishment comes from within.

Thomas Aquinas, in the thirteenth century, said that punishment has no effect unless the man who is punished accepts his punishment. A majority of prisoners today are not benefited by their punishment because they do not accept it, they only endure it.

I want to prove the failure of society to handle crime intelligently by citing three cases.

The case of Roger Haike shows the failure of the law.

The following case shows the failure of psychiatry.

Six young men, barely out of their teens, engaged in a contest known as the Chicken Toddle. Two automobiles were involved. It took place in flat, marshy country where two straight roads, raised above the swamp, intersected at right angles. At the intersection the two drivers synchronized their watches, drove for a mile from the crossing, and turned around. They could see each other across the intervening ground. At a minute agreed upon in advance, they started back toward the intersection. The purpose was to reach it, at a speed of not less than sixty miles per hour, at the same time. He who flinched and slowed down was Chicken, and the passengers acted as observers.

After the collision two of the passengers lay dead in the swamp and the others spent weeks in the hospital. The drivers walked away comparatively uninjured and were charged with aggravated assault and battery and involuntary manslaughter. It could have been second-degree murder, for the distinction in such cases is hairline.

They were sons of well-to-do people. One was the product of a broken home and had a personal record that was anything but reassuring. The other boy was spoiled and headstrong. They pleaded no defense.

These boys, being out on bail before trial, were sent to psychiatrists, four of whom testified. They did not agree about their patients' progress or about the length of time that further treatment should take, but they all felt that it would be a matter of years. The one thing they did agree upon was that the boys should not go to prison. They had even convinced the District Attorney.

Prison was, of course, the place where they had to go.

The case had been smothered in psychiatry, which is for the pure in heart who have been overburdened and genuinely distressed, not for those that use it as a device for getting out of a tight corner. The boys had not had security at home, and maybe, just maybe, the security of prison walls would work. Security need not be pleasant to be effective. But it was clear that the only thing not yet tried was the thing that happens to ordinary people when they kill other ordinary people. On balance there seemed nothing else to do.

When the trial was over, the judge was visited by a young couple who were relatives of one of the dead passengers. They were decent, sweetly behaved people with no vengeance in them. The girl had tears in her eyes and spoke of the defendants without anger. They wanted to give thanks for the outcome of the case, but their reason is what is important. They knew that the law could do nothing to bring the dead back to life. They did not want a life for a life: they did not want punishment in return for a crime, or if they did they did not say so in those terms. It was simply that any other solution would not have seemed right to them. They hunted hard for words to express the difficult idea that life requires a reaction equal to an action.

The problem arising out of that universal truth is the

form the reaction shall take. It is a tragedy of our generation that prison and punishment are the only reactions of size and shape sufficient to equalize a criminal act and appease its victims.

The following case shows the failure of the law, the failure of psychiatry, and the failure of humanity.

It is the case of Albert Fish, whose conviction and sentence of execution were affirmed, without opinion, by the New York Court of Appeals in 1935. It appears in the literature.[2]

Fish was a mild-mannered man approaching sixty, and father of six children. In 1928 he kidnapped, choked to death, and for nine days ate parts of Grace Budd, a girl of ten. While choking her he put his knee on her chest "to get her out of her misery." He was a religious fanatic, and in his confessions and statements to the doctor he made a point of religious atonement and self-castigation. There was no known form of perversion that he had not indulged in. He had eaten his own excrement. He had put cotton, saturated with alcohol, up his rectum and had set fire to it. X-rays showed twenty-nine needles inserted in his body between the scrotum

[2] Dr. Frederic Wertham: *The Show of Violence* (New York: Doubleday and Company; 1949); Giles Playfair and Derrick Sington: *The Offenders: The Case Against Legal Vengeance* (New York: Simon and Schuster; 1957).

and the anus. "If only pain were not so painful!" he exclaimed, when he spoke of his attempts to insert needles into the scrotum and beneath his nails.

It was finally discovered, too late, that Fish had molested at least one hundred children and that opportunity for cannibalism had presented itself in the five to fifteen child murders for which, after his arrest, it was estimated he was responsible.

He was no stranger to the law. He had been arrested eight times: for larceny, for bad checks, for sending obscene letters through the mails, for parole violations. Twice he was sent to psychiatric hospitals for observation, the first time over two years after he had killed and eaten Grace Budd. He was also picked up many times for impairing the morals of minors, but nothing much happened to him. He was generally let go because he was so kindly and co-operative and looked so innocent, the kind of man to whom anyone would entrust his child.

Four psychiatrists testified at his trial that he was sane, including the chief of the two public psychiatric hospitals where he had been observed and pronounced harmless *after* eating Grace. Some astonishing things were said. "Committing a crime has nothing to do with mental disease," was an example. Another was: "I know of individuals prominent in society: one ate human feces as a side dish with salad. I had a patient, a very prominent official, who did it."

The press shrilled loudly for revenge, and the jury obliged by giving Fish the death penalty. Interviewed later, a majority of the jury said that, while they thought him legally insane, they felt that he should die anyhow.

Fish went to his death coolly and even helped to strap on the leg electrodes.

He belongs in the class who should be killed if we are going to kill anybody, but, even so, the reasons are all twisted. He belongs with John Gilbert Graham, the airplane murderer, and with the low-grade mental defective who, a few years ago, escaped from the asylum for the criminal insane at Dartmoor, England, and murdered a child: he was found sane and hanged. Our real reason for killing such people is that we fear and hate them.

Fish was obviously incurable, unreformable, and unpunishable. If asked whether I would spare the life of such a monster, I should of course say that I would. The man was obviously mad and it was unfair to kill him. The failure to recognize him as mad is our fault, not his, and it is our responsibility to find a cure for him or to confine him and prevent his repeated aggressions. Killing him is to avoid the problem, not to solve it.

"To execute a sick man is like burning witches,"

Dr. Wertham wrote. I stand on that idea. These comments are what is in my mind and heart after four years as prosecutor, two summers as Voluntary Defender, and twenty-one years on the trial bench. I have sent too many people to prison to think that their problem can lie easy on the conscience of judges or of mankind.

To execute sick men or merely to incarcerate them is indeed like burning witches or chaining them to the wall. If you say that there are no more witches, how eagerly you take the bait! It will not be long, God willing, before you say that there are no more criminals either, but only sick men, socially or medically or both.

Let us remember what we are about. The whole legal system rests upon public approval and consent. That is one of its greatest beauties. We have been talking about the law, but we cannot separate the law from our way of life within the whole family of man. There must be, as Holmes put it, a sense of the infinite in our work, and the world of man must become one world and one spirit. It cannot be saved on any other basis. We have fought our wars hitherto for territory with the notions that go with territory, but the enemy and the territory of the future is in the mind of man. From now on we must fight from behind the frontier of our prejudice against the prejudice of our enemy, and the ancient weapons will no longer work. We cannot kill an idea with a bayonet. We cannot put handcuffs on a gale of wind. We can fight an idea only with a better idea, with less prejudice, wiser procedures, and a cleaner purpose that man shall be wholly free, in his body and, even more urgently, in his mind. He is not free if he is punished and imprisoned, and if he is not free he is a slave.

Our law cannot stand for slavery. It must stand for the truth and justice, in lower case, that do happen between man and man.

Alan Paton has given us a closing text:

> *An offender must be punished. . . . I don't argue about that. But to punish and not to restore, that is the greatest of all offenses. . . . If man takes unto himself God's right to punish, then he must also take upon himself God's promise to restore. . . . There's a hard law, that when a deep injury is done to us, we never recover until we forgive.*

To end with, let us remember that there is much love about, and that hatred is for those who are too weak to love. We can use the public, with its decency and its love, to counteract its hatred and its crime, and we do not always know just where to seek for the precise solutions. There are lovely surprises, and we must allow for them. Let me close with the account of one, as told by Kenyon J. Scudder,[3] first Superintendent of Chino:

It is the story of two men in a railroad train. One was so reserved that his companion had difficulty in persuading him to talk about himself. He was, he said at length, a convict returning from five years' imprisonment in a distant prison, but his people were too poor to visit him and were too uneducated to be very articulate on paper. Hence he had written to them to make a sign for him when he was released and came home. If they wanted him they should put a white ribbon in the big apple tree which stood close to the railroad track at the bottom of the garden, and he would get off the train, but if they did not want him they were to do nothing and he would stay on the train and seek a new life elsewhere. He said that they were nearing his home town and that he couldn't bear to look. His new friend said that he would look and took his place by the window to watch for the apple tree which the other had described to him.

In a minute he put a hand on his companion's arm. "There it is," he cried. "It's all right! The whole tree is white with ribbons."

[3] His book, *Prisoners Are People* (New York: Doubleday and Company; 1952), should be required reading on the subject of penology.

A NOTE ON THE AUTHOR

Curtis Bok was born in Wyncote, Pennsylvania, in 1897. He is the son of Edward Bok, famous editor and author, whose The Americanization of Edward Bok *was awarded the Pulitzer Prize in 1921. He attended the Hill School and in 1915 entered Williams College. Two years later he withdrew to serve in the First World War. On his return, he matriculated at the University of Virginia Law School, completing his course there in 1921. He then embarked on the practice of law. In 1936 he became Judge of the Orphans Court of Philadelphia County, and the following year President Judge of the Court of Common Pleas No. 6. He was elected in the autumn of 1958 to the Supreme Court of Pennsylvania. He is married and has two sons and three daughters.*

A NOTE ON THE TYPE

The text of this book is set in Caledonia, *a Linotype face that belongs to the family of printing types called "modern face" by printers—a term used to mark the change in style of type-letters that occurred about 1800. Caledonia borders on the general design of Scotch Modern, but is more freely drawn than that letter.*

The book was composed, printed, and bound by The Plimpton Press, Norwood, Mass. The paper was made by S. D. Warren Co., Boston. The typography and binding are based on original designs by W. A. Dwiggins.